EINSTEIN'S

WHO, WHAT, AND WHERE

Book 2

Carol Einstein

EDUCATORS PUBLISHING SERVICE
Cambridge and Toronto

ACKNOWLEDGMENTS

To Bernice and Herman Einstein, who first encouraged me
to take an interest in the world around me.

To my colleagues, friends, and family: Joan Amron, Susanna Einstein,
Maureen Farbstein, Marilyn Heineman, Marcia Kessler, Debbie Lemchen, Bonnie Long,
Kathi Ramos, and Annette Rodriguez. When time is so precious, you were
always willing to listen and to help. Thank you.

To my students, who told me so frankly what they thought of my ideas and stories.
Your honesty and your expertise are much appreciated.

With special thanks to my ever skillful editor, Mary Troeger,
who so tactfully clarified my thoughts and who always catches my errors.
Your enthusiasm and true interest in the subject matter are much appreciated.

Art Director: Jan Shapiro
Maps by Lucidity Information Design, LLC
Editor: Mary Troeger
Managing Editor: Sheila Neylon

Printed in U.S.A.
ISBN 0-8388-2652-0
978-0-8388-2652-2

4 5 6 7 PP 10 09 08 07

To my husband and son, who give me such joy and who always encourage me to take that extra step.

With thanks and love,
C.S.E.

Contents

New York City

Dear Reader,

When I was a child, the world seemed much bigger; traveling by airplane was an exciting event. I was a very lucky child. My grandmother lived in Switzerland, and my family would visit her during the summer. After spending time at her home, we would often travel to another country. I loved visiting these new places; they were so different from New York City. As we traveled, my mother always told me wonderful stories about the places we were visiting and the famous events that had happened there. I learned a great deal from these trips. One of the most important things I learned was that the world is full of interesting people, places, and events. I still think this is true, and I'd like to share with you some of these amazing stories.

I hope you enjoy reading them and find them as fascinating as I did.

Carol Einstein

The NAZCA LINES

Think about It ....

Why do you think people would create a design so large that they could not see it completely?

____

____

AS YOU READ Put a ★ beside each important idea in the story. Then write in the margin why each is important. Put a ✓ next to parts of the story that you find interesting. Put a **?** next to parts of the story you do not understand.

OTES

In the southern desert of Peru, about twelve miles from the town of Nazca, hundreds of huge drawings have been formed in the dry earth. People made these lines long ago by removing the surface layer of stones and piling them up like a wall along the edges of the cleared space. Some of these clearings are over half a mile long. They are known as the Nazca Lines. Covering an area two hundred miles square, these drawings include both geometric designs and figures of animals, birds, fish, and insects. Scientists believe that the Nazca people created the lines about two thousand years ago, but little is known about them. Because this area of Peru gets almost no rain, few people live there and the lines have been left undisturbed for the most part. Since they are so large, people get a much better view of them from the air. The smallest animal figure is eighty feet long and the largest is nine hundred feet. We still do not know why a group of people would bother to make drawings that they would never be able to see as a whole. It remains one of the world's great mysteries.

It was not until the 1920s, when planes started flying between Lima, Peru's capital, and Arequipa, a city to the south, that people became aware of the drawings.

Pilots and airline passengers often got glimpses of large cleared geometric shapes in the Nazca region, and soon people were calling them "prehistoric airstrips." A well-known Peruvian archaeologist, Mejia Xesspe, explored the area in 1927. He believed the lines were ancient roads that had been used for religious or ceremonial purposes. In 1939, he published a short description of what he had found with a plan showing thirteen major clusters of drawings, but very few people were interested in his findings.

Then in 1941 Paul Kosok, an American history professor, who was in Peru studying ancient methods of **irrigation,** made an important discovery. When he and his wife, Rose, were visiting the Nazca area, they went out for a walk, which brought them up to a stony **plateau**, with a central cleared spot. From there many straight lines branched off in different directions. Below the plateau, the plain stretched away for several miles to the east. There they discovered more lines and several large cleared rectangular shapes. Next to one of these shapes, the Kosoks noticed a faint outline. After more exploration, they realized that this was part of an enormous drawing, 150 feet across. When Paul Kosok plotted the picture on paper, he saw that it was a strange image of a bird.

Later the Kosoks returned to the central spot so that they could watch the sunset. Rose Kosok noticed that the sun was setting almost exactly over the end of one of the lines. The couple remembered that it was June 22, the shortest day of the year in the Southern **Hemisphere**, and the day when the sun rises and sets at its most northern point along the **horizon**. They thought that the ancient Nazcas had constructed this line to mark the summer **solstice** and guessed that perhaps the "largest astronomy book in the world was spread out in front of them."

After Kosok looked at photos of the markings taken from a plane, he found about a dozen similar "centers," where lines moved outward across the plateau like the spokes of a wheel. Kosok had only a short time before he had to return to his teaching job in the United States, so he took some compass readings of lines at a few of these centers. After he saw these measurements, Kosok was convinced that there were more solstice lines and that certain orientations, or directions, were repeated at different spots. Before he left for the United States, he asked Maria Reiche, a German math teacher living in Lima, to continue his work.

Right from the beginning, Reiche was fascinated by the drawings. Late in 1941, she observed the sun setting along the lines around the time of the winter solstice, December 22, the longest day of the year in the Southern Hemisphere. Because of this, Reiche agreed with the Kosoks that the mysterious lines had something to do with keeping a calendar, perhaps for the farmers living long ago.

Reiche moved to Nazca in 1946. She spent more than fifty years charting and photographing the Nazca drawings and fighting for their protection. Over the centuries the wind had swept away the **exposed** light-colored soil, and many of the narrow lines had become very faint. When she started her work in 1946, only the major lines, triangles, and four-sided figures could be spotted from the air. Reiche decided that she would clean the lines, and as she did this she discovered all kinds of additional figures and designs. At first, Reiche used a rake to remove the dark pebbles on top, which left the fresh clay underneath revealed. But finding this too rough, she started using a broom to lightly sweep the surface. To make sure she was following the true outline of the figure, she returned to it at different times of the day as the light changed. Often a cleaning would take days or even weeks, but Reiche enjoyed the time in the desert, often sleeping under the stars and living on a simple diet of fruits and nuts.

The Peruvian air force sent their training flights over the desert. Photographs taken on these flights began to document how the lines looked from the air. Still this was not enough for Reiche. When one of the first helicopters arrived in Peru, she reserved it so that she could get a closer view of the drawings.

Reiche discovered many different animal shapes. She found eighteen examples of birds, a monkey that was over three hundred feet across, three examples of fish, a pair of llamas, two lizards, and a dog. Except for the llamas, all the animal shapes were made with unbroken lines that never crossed one another. However, she found that there were many more single straight lines, geometric drawings, and cleared areas than animal figures. Spirals were the most common of all single-line figures. Reiche found one hundred of them. Some were **crudely** designed, but others were beautifully made. One example was a huge double spiral whose diameter was about three hundred feet and each turn nearly ten feet wide.

She noticed that there were very few pictures having to do with humans. She did find one design suggesting a human, but its outstretched hands had only nine fingers. She also discovered a few strange figures that look almost like cartoons of humans. These designs were on the sides of steep hills, and nothing like them appears on the plateau where the other drawings are found. Scientists suggest that they may have been done at a different time from the main drawings or that it is just harder to make a neat outline on a steep slope.

After years of studying the lines, Reiche agreed with the Kosoks' original idea that the markings were a huge sky calendar, which was important to the farmers working in such a harsh environment. She concluded that the sketches corresponded to the positions of different groups of stars in the sky. Over the years, there have been many other theories about the lines. Since there are no surviving Nazcas and no known written record of their culture, we will most likely never know why they were created. What we do know is that the Nazca Lines are **unique.** In 1968, Reiche wrote a book about them, *Mystery on the Desert.* Knowing that just one car or jeep driven across the stones could destroy the lines, she used the money she earned from the book to pay for guards who would protect them. As Reiche explained, "This precious thing should be treated like a very fragile manuscript that is guarded in a special room in a library."

irrigation *n.* the process of supplying water to land or crops by using a system of ditches, pipes, or canals

plateau *n.* an area of flat land that is higher than the surrounding country

hemisphere *n.* one half of the earth (northern, southern, eastern, or western)

horizon *n.* the line where the sky and the ground or the sea seem to meet

solstice *n.* either of the two times of the year when the sun reaches its farthest northern or southern point in the sky. The winter solstice, about December 21, marks the longest night of the year in the Northern Hemisphere. The summer solstice, about June 22, marks the longest day of the year in the Northern Hemisphere.

expose *v.* to leave open, uncovered or without protection

crudely *adv.* done or made without skill; roughly

unique *adj.* not having an equal; being the only one of its kind

LOOKING BACK AT WHAT YOU HAVE READ

1. What are the Nazca Lines?

____

____

2. What was the first drawing that Paul Kosok discovered in the desert?

____

____

3. List in order the people who saw the Nazca Lines and tell what they thought they were.

____

____

____

4. Sometimes something happens just by chance. In this story, what happens just by chance?

____

____

5. What do you think may happen to the lines?

6. The Kosoks and Maria Reiche believed that the drawings were pictures of the positions of different groups of stars in the sky. What other theory could there be to explain what the lines represent?

7. Why do you think Maria Reiche devoted fifty years of her life to the Nazca Lines?

WORKING WITH WORDS

Write down four words from the story whose meaning you do not know. If a word is not a vocabulary word, look up the definition and write it down. Use each of the words in a sentence.

A **simile** is a phrase or expression introduced by the words *like* or *as*. It compares two things that are not alike.

Example: She has such a bad cold that her voice sounds *as rough as sandpaper.*

Explain what the simile above means. Then try to make a new sentence using this simile.

Now explain what the following similes mean and try using them in sentences.

When Paul Kosok asked Maria Reiche to continue his work, she accepted *as quick as a wink.*

Maria's new job fit *like a glove.*

After a day's work on the desert, Reiche slept *like a baby.*

CROSSWORD PUZZLE

Use the clues to fill in the puzzle. Then check your answers with each clue. Do they make sense?

Down

1. Many of the drawings in the desert are examples of __________.

2. Maria Reiche hired guards to __________ the lines.

3. When Maria Reiche lived on the desert, she did not have this for her bath.

4. An area of flat land that is higher than the surrounding country

5. One of a kind

6. The day of the year when the sun reaches its farthest northern or southern point in the sky

10. A method to supply water to farmland by using canals and ditches

11. A synonym for *very old*

12. The capital of Peru

13. The opposite of *morning*

15. The last name of a well-known Peruvian archaeologist

Across

2. Some of the first people to see the drawings from the air

4. The country where the Nazca Lines are located

7. The first name of Paul Kosok's wife

8. A tool used by Maria Reiche to clean the lines

9. The most common kind of figure made with single lines

14. To find something

16. There are hundreds of these in the desert, showing animals and geometric shapes.

17. The name of the people who made the lines

WRITING SKILLS

The amazing Nazca Lines were discovered by chance. Write a paragraph about the lines. Be sure to answer these five questions.

What are the Nazca Lines? Where are they? When were they discovered?

Who were the major figures in the history of the Nazca Lines? Why are they famous?

Be sure that your paragraph has a title, a topic sentence, which gives the main idea of the paragraph, and a concluding sentence, which lets the reader know that you have finished your discussion.

First, write down some key ideas. When you have finished your paragraph, proofread your writing. Does it make sense? Have you included everything you wanted to say? Check it for correct spelling, grammar, capitalization, and punctuation.

Key ideas

Title:

Maria Reiche had an amazing life in Peru. Write a paragraph about her life. Why do you think it was amazing? Use examples from the story for your supporting ideas.

Be sure that your paragraph has a title, a topic sentence, which gives the main idea of the paragraph, and a concluding sentence, which lets the reader know that you have finished your discussion.

First, write down some key ideas. When you have finished your paragraph, proofread your writing. Does it make sense? Have you included everything you wanted to say? Check it for correct spelling, grammar, capitalization, and punctuation.

Key ideas

Title:

The Publication of *UNCLE TOM'S CABIN*

Think about It ....

What conditions exist today that you think are inhuman?

____

____

AS YOU READ Put a ★ beside each important idea in the story. Then write in the margin why each is important. Put a ✓ next to parts of the story that you find interesting. Put a **?** next to parts of the story you do not understand.

OTES

When Harriet Beecher Stowe's novel *Uncle Tom's Cabin* was published in 1852, it was an immediate **sensation**. Using events from newspaper reports and stories told by escaped slaves, Stowe created a tale of people living in the terrible conditions of slavery. Her characters were like real people to her readers. The story begins on a day in February. A slave owner in Kentucky, who needs money to pay a debt, chooses to sell two of his slaves: Uncle Tom, his best worker, and Harry, a clever, handsome little boy. When Harry's mother, Eliza Harris, hears that her son will be sold and taken away the next day, she flees with him. Harris reaches the half-frozen Ohio River with many men in pursuit. Holding her son, she jumps from one large piece of ice to another until she reaches the opposite side of the river. From there the two of them make their way to Canada and freedom.

On the other hand, Uncle Tom, a faithful, caring person, decides not to run away. Tom finds out that if he and Harry are not sold, the owner will have to sell his land and all the slaves. So when Tom's wife, Chloe, begs him to try to escape to Canada where he would be free, Tom says, "I never have broke trust. . . . It's better for me alone to go, than to break up the place and sell all." For a time, Tom lives with a kind master and can write to his wife, whom he was forced to leave behind.

However, after this master dies, a vicious plantation owner in Louisiana buys Tom. The new owner orders Tom to whip another slave for not picking enough cotton, but Tom says no and is kicked and whipped. Later, the owner orders Tom to tell him where some runaway slaves are hiding, but Tom refuses. In a fury, the owner kills him. Stowe painted such a lifelike picture of the suffering of each slave that many readers cried as they read the story.

Just two years before the book was published, the **Fugitive** Slave Law was passed. This new law deeply angered many people in the North. Not only did it say that all citizens, whether living in the North or South, had to turn in runaway slaves, but the law also took away a person's individual rights. An accused person did not have the right to a court appearance where the truth of a case would be decided; this was a basic right in the United States. People who gave shelter, food, or any other help to an escaping slave could be fined a thousand dollars and put in prison for six months. The government appointed marshals to make sure that the law was carried out. The law **penalized** citizens who helped runaways as well as marshals who did not seize fugitives.

Not long after this law was passed, African Americans who had escaped their masters were kidnapped in increasing numbers and forced to return to slavery. Stowe, a teacher and author, was very upset by what was happening and raged against the "cool way" the newspapers described this terrible situation. **Abolitionist** newspapers printed articles telling their readers how they could **resist** the law. Abolitionist groups also raised money to help African Americans buy their freedom.

For eighteen years Stowe had lived in Cincinnati, Ohio, only a river's width away from Kentucky, a state that allowed slavery. She had seen for herself the cruelty and horrors of slavery. Stowe decided that she would write a story that would move others to share her anger. Until the Fugitive Slave Law was passed, Stowe explained, "I have always felt that I had no particular call to **meddle** with this subject. . . . But I feel now that the time is come when even a woman or a child who can speak a word for freedom and humanity is bound to speak."

Stowe started writing *Uncle Tom's Cabin*. Beginning in June 1851, it was published in installments in the *National Era*, an abolitionist newspaper. It was filled with **vivid** descriptions, and readers loved it. When Stowe was late sending in an installment and the newspaper appeared without her latest story, it was flooded with complaints. Never before had an American newspaper received so much mail when a story was late. When Stowe tried to get her book published, though, the first publisher turned it down, explaining that a novel by a woman would be too risky. At that time, few women wrote novels, and those that were published often appeared under a man's name. Then John Jewett, a brave young publisher and strong abolitionist, told Stowe he would be honored to print her novel. The book was so long that it was published in two volumes. Jewett worried that people would not want to buy such a long book.

The novel came out just twelve days before the series in the *National Era* ended. Many people were upset by the Fugitive Slave Law. But when they read *Uncle Tom's Cabin*, filled with powerful descriptions of slave life, they were overwhelmed. Never before had a novel been so popular. In less than two months, the publisher sold fifty thousand sets of the book–a total of one hundred thousand books. The demand was so great that eight printing presses were running throughout the year, day and night, to print it. During the first year alone, three hundred thousand copies were sold in the United States. In Britain, where books were much cheaper, more than a million and a half copies were sold.

Almost as soon as the novel appeared, it was translated into more than a dozen languages and was made into a play. An entire New York City theater audience fell silent as Eliza and her son escaped from slave catchers and reached the northern side of the river and freedom; at the end of the play people were in tears. Songs, toys, and little figures based on the story were sold throughout the northern part of the United States and in Great Britain. Abolitionists praised the book and its author, describing it as a work of genius sent from God to open the hearts and minds of white people. But in the southern part of the United States where slavery was a way of life, both the book and the author were strongly criticized. Slave owners said it was filled with lies and an incorrect view of slavery. Southerners tried to stop the sale of the book. In Mobile, Alabama, a bookseller was run out of town for displaying the novel in his shop. But such actions only made the work more popular elsewhere.

Stowe's book was so successful that she became the most powerful voice speaking out for slaves. *Uncle Tom's Cabin* had an influence that very few other novels have ever had. Not only did it appeal to abolitionists, a very small group of people, it also affected all Americans. It helped to **solidify** both supporters and opponents of slavery. Those who were in favor of slavery believed that the book painted an unfair picture of how the system worked. They were especially annoyed by the book's success in Great Britain, a country that Southerners considered a friend of the South. In the North, people already disturbed by the Fugitive Slave Law became more convinced of the evils of slavery. Stowe had never been a member of an anti-slavery group, and women were not encouraged to discuss such issues in public. However, when two Scottish antislavery groups invited her to speak about her book, she made a tour of Great Britain in 1853. Wherever she and her family went, crowds of people greeted her. Large public meetings were held in her honor. In Glasgow, Scotland, two thousand people came to see her.

Uncle Tom's Cabin divided people–those who were against slavery and those who supported it. The book helped fan the flames that were to explode in the Civil War. The effect of *Uncle Tom's Cabin* on the United States was so great that when Stowe visited Abraham Lincoln at the White House in 1862, Lincoln was said to have greeted her with these words, "So you're the little woman who wrote the book that made this great war."

sensation *n.* a person or event that causes great excitement or interest

fugitive *n.* a person who is running away, especially from the police

penalize *v.* to give a penalty or punishment to

abolitionist *n.* a person who actively supported the ending of slavery and the slave trade, especially in the United States

resist *v.* to oppose or go against; to not accept

meddle *v.* to concern oneself with or intrude in the affairs of others without having been asked

vivid *adj.* making a clear or lifelike image in the mind

solidify *v.* to make secure or firmly fixed; to become solid

LOOKING BACK AT WHAT YOU HAVE READ

1. Why did Harriet Stowe decide to write *Uncle Tom's Cabin*?

___

___

___

2. Where had Stowe witnessed slavery?

___

___

3. Why was *Uncle Tom's Cabin* such a popular book?

___

___

4. How do we know that *Uncle Tom's Cabin* was a popular book?

___

___

5. What was the Fugitive Slave Law and what were its effects on people?

___

___

___

6. How did Americans feel about the Fugitive Slave Law?

____

____

____

7. How did the publication of *Uncle Tom's Cabin* change Stowe's life?

____

____

____

8. Why was *Uncle Tom's Cabin* such an important book?

____

____

____

WORKING WITH WORDS

When Uncle Tom's Cabin was published, people had different reactions to it. Often, people living in the South felt differently from people living in the North. Make a list of **adjectives** that would describe reactions of Southerners and Northerners, both positive and negative. For each category, try to think of at least six adjectives.

Positive reactions

_______________ _______________

_______________ _______________

_______________ _______________

_______________ _______________

Negative reactions

______________________ ______________________

______________________ ______________________

______________________ ______________________

______________________ ______________________

______________________ ______________________

A **synonym** is a word that has the same or almost the same meaning as another word.

A *gift* and a *present* are synonyms.

Think of synonyms for the following words. If you can, write two.

vicious ______________________ ______________________

praised ______________________ ______________________

angered ______________________ ______________________

faithful ______________________ ______________________

clever ______________________ ______________________

incorrect ______________________ ______________________

risky ______________________ ______________________

upset ______________________ ______________________

Words may have more than one meaning.

Example: The movie was an immediate **sensation**.

In the sentence, *sensation* means a cause of excitement.

Sensation can also mean a feeling.

In the following sentences, the word in bold print has one meaning. Write what it is. Then see if you can write another meaning the word may have.

Stowe described the terrible **conditions** of slavery.

"I never have **broke** trust."

Tom is **whipped** when he refuses to whip another slave.

Many of her readers **cried** as they read the story.

Stowe raged against the "**cool** way" the newspapers described this terrible situation.

Stowe decided that she would write a story that would **move** others to share her anger.

WRITING SKILLS

When *Uncle Tom's Cabin* was published, many people thought it was a work of genius. Pretend that you are a newspaper reporter living during Stowe's time and that you have just finished reading *Uncle Tom's Cabin*. Write a newspaper article praising the book and its author. Your article will be in paragraph form. Use as many paragraphs as you need. Be sure that your article has a title and that each paragraph has a topic sentence, which gives the main idea.

First, write down some key ideas. When you have finished your article, proofread your writing. Does it make sense? Have you included everything you wanted to say? Check it for correct spelling, grammar, capitalization, and punctuation.

Key ideas

Title:

Many people also thought that *Uncle Tom's Cabin* showed an unfair picture of slavery. Pretend you are one of these people and write a letter to a newspaper that has just given the book a glowing review. Be sure to explain why you do not agree with the review.

First, write down some key ideas. When you have finished your letter, proofread your writing. Does it make sense? Have you included everything you wanted to say? Check it for correct spelling, grammar, capitalization, and punctuation.

Key ideas

Dear ____________________,

Sincerely,

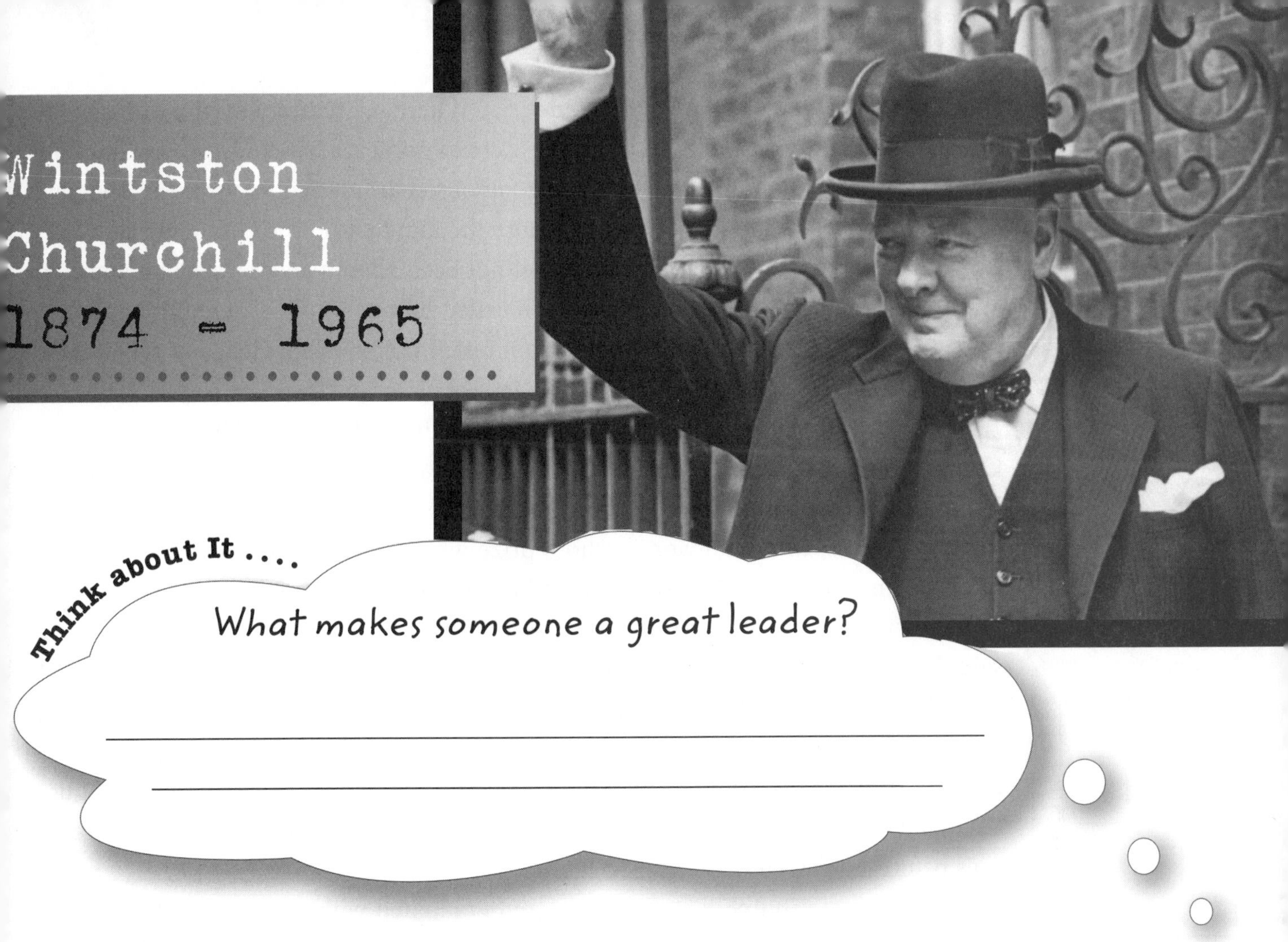

Wintston Churchill 1874 – 1965

Think about It ....

What makes someone a great leader?

____

____

AS YOU READ Put a ★ beside each important idea in the story. Then write in the margin why each is important. Put a ✓ next to parts of the story that you find interesting. Put a ? next to parts of the story you do not understand.

OTES

Winston Churchill was one of the great world leaders of the twentieth century. He was an extraordinary speaker and writer whose energy, imagination, and boldness aided his country at a time when it most needed help. Early in World War II, after Hitler had conquered most of Europe, Britain stood alone against the Nazis. Churchill is remembered as the fearless prime minister of Great Britain who **defied** Adolf Hitler. When many people thought that the Nazis would defeat Britain, Churchill's speeches inspired the British to "their finest hour" and finally to victory.

Churchill was born at Blenheim Palace, the 320-room home of his grandfather, the Duke of Marlborough. His father, Lord Randolph Churchill, was a well-known English politician, and his American mother, Jennie Jerome, was famous for her beauty and wit. Churchill was a small, red-haired boy with blue eyes and freckles, who talked with a **stutter** and a **lisp**. His greatest pleasure was reading. He adored his parents, but they led busy lives and spent little time with him. In his autobiography, Churchill said that he was what adults called "a troublesome boy." He was not doing bad things, but his stubbornness and high spirits annoyed people.

At the age of seven, Churchill was sent to boarding school. Later he wrote, "My teachers saw me at once backward and **precocious**, reading books beyond my years, and yet at the bottom of the Form [grade]. . . . Where my reason, imagination or interest were not **engaged**, I would not or I could not learn." In 1887, when Churchill was twelve, he was admitted to Harrow, a famous boarding school for boys. The head of the school, Dr. Welldon, decided to ignore the fact that on the entrance exam Churchill handed in a blank paper. He had not been able to answer a single question on the Latin paper. Years later, Churchill recalled that he knew a lot about history, poetry, and writing essays but that the exam tested only his knowledge of Latin and math. He entered as the lowest boy in the lowest class, and there he stayed.

At Harrow, the boys at the top of their class learned Latin and Greek, but Churchill and his classmates at the bottom learned English. "We were considered such **dunces** that we could learn only English." Yet at the same time that he was in the lowest class, Churchill won a school prize when he recited without error twelve hundred lines of "Lays of Ancient Rome," a very popular poem.

Following Harrow, Churchill entered Sandhurst, the West Point of Britain. He said that he became interested in an army career because of his toy soldiers. As a child, he had fifteen hundred of them, all British and all the same size. He delighted in lining them up and planning battles. His father, Lord Randolph, agreed with his decision to enter the army. He had hoped that his son would become a lawyer, but Churchill's school record was too poor for that. Even then, it took Churchill three tries before he passed the entrance exam.

At Sandhurst, Churchill studied hard and graduated with honors in 1894, standing eighth in a class of one hundred and fifty. He was assigned to the **cavalry**. After a brief time in England, he was attached as an "observer," or reporter, to a Spanish force that had been sent to Cuba in 1895 to put down a rebellion. While he was there, he earned money by sending back colorful reports to a newspaper in London. This was the beginning of a lifelong career in writing.

After Cuba, Churchill received assignments as both a soldier and a reporter in many different parts of the vast British Empire. He was involved in heavy fighting in India and took part in one of the last great cavalry charges at Omdurman in the Sudan. Then in 1899, Churchill resigned from the army and wrote a book about his adventures. He ran for a seat in **Parliament**, in the House of Commons, but was narrowly defeated. The same year a war started between the British and the Boers, Dutch settlers in South Africa. Churchill, who was always adventurous, traveled there as a reporter for one of the London newspapers. He was captured by the Boers not long after his arrival, but he made a surprising, nighttime escape from a prisoner-of-war camp by climbing up the prison wall and walking out past the guards. Because various newspapers told of his great escape, Churchill returned home a famous hero and won election to the House of Commons at the age of twenty-six. This began a career in politics that would occupy him, along with writing, for the rest of his life.

In 1911, Churchill was made First Lord of the Admiralty, the highest position in the British navy. He feared that there might be a war with Germany, so he prepared the British fleet. It was ready in 1914 when World War I began. In 1924, he was named Chancellor of the Exchequer, where he was in charge of managing the country's money. This was the second highest job in the government. When his party, the Conservatives, did not win the 1929 election, he lost his job as chancellor. However, he kept his seat in the House of Commons.

During the 1930s, antiwar feeling was strong in Britain. Prime Minister Stanley Baldwin believed that the British people wanted peace at almost any price. He avoided challenging the aggressive actions of Hitler, the Nazi leader of Germany. Churchill, however, thought that the nation should be awakened to the possibility of another world war. Many times, both in the House of Commons and in his newspaper articles, Churchill warned about the threat from Nazi Germany, but hardly anyone listened. In the Commons he roared, "Arm." When Hitler took over most of Czechoslovakia in March 1939, Churchill declared that other countries would be next. Still the Commons did not listen to him. Historians now believe that at any of a dozen points Hitler could have been stopped without bloodshed. In every case, Churchill had pleaded in vain for action.

In September 1939, Germany marched into Poland, and World War II began. Prime Minister Neville Chamberlain named Churchill First Lord of the Admiralty. As the House of Commons was listening to the news that war had begun, Churchill walked into the House. There was thunderous applause from everyone, welcoming him back to his old naval job. The following spring, Chamberlain was forced to resign. Churchill was asked to form a government, and he gave a stirring address to the House of Commons. He told them, "I have nothing to offer but blood, toil, and sweat. . . . You ask: 'What is our aim?' I can answer in one word: 'Victory!' Victory at all costs, victory in spite of all terror, victory however long and hard the road may be."

Churchill's energy and his stubborn refusal to make peace until Hitler was crushed were extremely important in arousing and maintaining British resistance to Germany. Hoping to break the British spirit, the Germans began bombing England in 1940 and continued air raids into 1941. They attacked not only military targets but also cities. In some of the raids as many as 1,400 civilians were killed, most of them in London. Even during air-raid alarms, Churchill went into the streets as the bombs fell. Everywhere he went, he held up two fingers in a "V-for-victory" salute, giving the country hope. His speeches rallied the people from feelings of defeat and despair. During six years of war, Churchill never seemed to get tired. He worked late into the night and traveled thousands of miles. When the United States and the Soviet Union became Britain's partners, he provided the leadership to make sure that the three nations worked together.

Finally, on May 7, 1945, almost five years to the day after Churchill became prime minister, Germany surrendered. Within two months, Churchill's party was voted out of office. Although Churchill was respected, the British blamed the Conservatives for not being prepared for World War II, and they wanted the broad social changes that the Labour Party promised. Churchill was bitterly disappointed, but he took his place as leader of the opposition in the House of Commons. In 1951, at almost seventy-seven, he became prime minister again when the Conservative Party returned to power. Churchill had told the British people, "It is the last big prize I seek to win." In 1953, Churchill, the author of many historical works and biographies, was awarded the Nobel Prize for literature. In 1955, he retired as prime minister but kept his seat in the Commons. Churchill's remarkable career ended in 1964 when he decided not to run in the general election. The following year he died at the age of ninety. For many, nothing expressed their feeling of loss better than Shakespeare's words "When comes such another?"

defy *v.* to resist boldly

stutter *n.* a way of speaking that has many pauses and repetitions of sounds

lisp *n.* a way of speaking in which the sounds *s* and *z* are pronounced like the *t* in the word thick

precocious *adj.* showing skills or abilities at an earlier age than is usual

engage *v.* to attract and hold someone's attention; to involve

dunce *n.* a stupid person

cavalry *n.* in earlier times, soldiers trained to fight on horseback; in modern times, soldiers trained to fight from tanks or helicopters

Parliament *n.* the two groups of lawmakers that govern Great Britain, the House of Commons and the House of Lords

LOOKING BACK AT WHAT YOU HAVE READ

1. In what ways was Churchill an unusual student?

____

____

2. Do you think that Dr. Welldon was right to admit Churchill to Harrow? Explain your answer.

____

____

3. Why did Churchill go into the army?

____

____

4. How did Churchill change when he went to Sandhurst?

____

____

5. How do we know that as a young man Churchill was very adventurous?

____

____

6. When did World War II start?

____

____

7. How did Churchill help the British people during World War II?

____

____

8. For how many years did Churchill serve in the House of Commons?

____

____

WORKING WITH WORDS

Word Puzzle

Using the letters in the word PARLIAMENT, see how many small words you can make. You may use a letter twice in your word if it appears twice in this word.

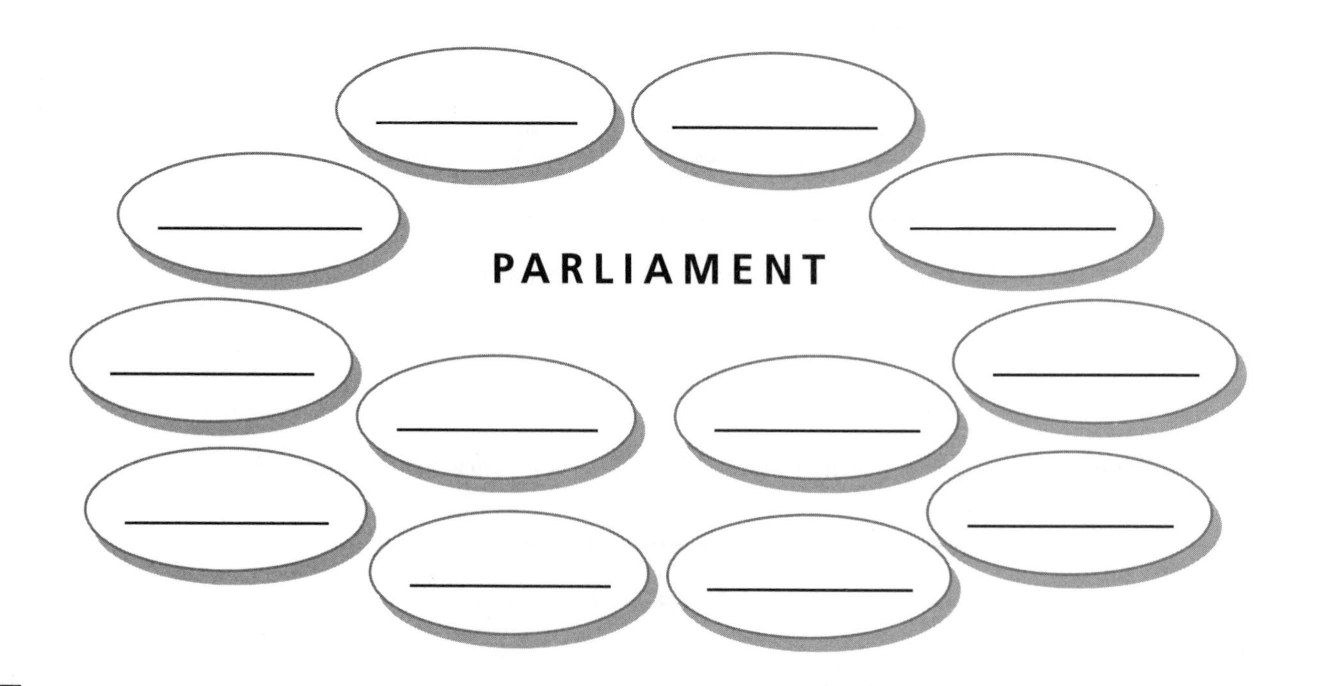

An **idiom** is a group of words that have a special meaning. If you do not know the special meaning, you will not understand what a person is saying. It may even sound ridiculous.
For example, "On the house." This means that something is free.

Read the explanations of the following idioms. Then write a sentence using the idiom.

The idiom "uphill battle" means to face a very difficult task.

____

____

The idiom "to not have a prayer" means to not have any chance.

____

____

The idiom "throw your hat in the ring" means to try to get elected.

____

____

Write down four words from the story whose meaning you do not know. If a word is not a vocabulary word, look up the definition and write it down. Use each of the words in a sentence.

__________ __________ __________ __________

____

____

____

____

____

____

____

____

WRITING SKILLS

Write a paragraph summarizing the important events of Winston Churchill's life. Put the events in chronological order. Be sure that your paragraph has a topic sentence, which gives the main idea of the paragraph, and a concluding sentence, which lets the reader know that you have finished your discussion.

First, write down some key ideas. When you have finished the paragraph, proofread your writing. Does it make sense? Have you included everything you wanted to say? Check it for correct spelling, grammar, capitalization, and punctuation.

Key ideas

Important Events in Churchill's Life

Churchill said that he first became interested in the army because of his toy soldiers. What first sparked an interest or a hobby in your life? Was it a compact disc, a camera, a toy figure, a special gift from your family or a friend? Please write about one of your interests or hobbies. Be sure that your paragraph has a title, a topic sentence, which gives the main idea of the paragraph, and a concluding sentence, which lets the reader know that you have finished your discussion.

First, write down some key ideas. When you have finished your paragraph, proofread your writing. Does it make sense? Have you included everything you wanted to say? Check it for correct spelling, grammar, capitalization, and punctuation.

Key ideas

Title:

The SILK ROAD

Think about It . . . .

Before European explorers discovered a sea route to China, how did Chinese goods come to Europe?

AS YOU READ Put a ★ beside each important idea in the story. Then write in the margin why each is important. Put a ✓ next to parts of the story that you find interesting. Put a ? next to parts of the story you do not understand.

OTES

Stretching from China to the Mediterranean Sea was an impressive system of trade routes that became known as the Silk Road. Over hundreds of years, contacts slowly developed among kingdoms and tribes, and a number of routes, which **caravans** followed, connected China with these kingdoms and tribes of Central Asia, India, and Persia. During the Han Empire, which lasted from 206 B.C. to A.D. 220, this set of roads even connected the two most powerful states of their time, the Roman Empire in the West and China in the East. Between these two distant states, other powerful kingdoms, such as Parthia (now part of Iran) and India, and important trading centers, such as Constantinople and Baghdad, also exchanged goods and ideas.

Although some trade routes had existed for several centuries, in 139 B.C., the Han emperor Wudi sent his representative Zhang Qian across China on a secret mission to faraway and unexplored areas in the West. Thirteen years later, Zhang returned to the city of Chang'an (today's Xi'an) to report to the emperor. He had much to tell because twice he had been captured and twice he had escaped from enemy forces. He described to the emperor a new world with a great variety of goods and populations; he told him about rich and previously unknown kingdoms. For the first time, Emperor Wudi learned of the existence of Parthia and of another far-off country called Li-jien, which may have been Rome. Zhang visited Fergana (now in Central Asia, just northeast of Afghanistan) where he saw people riding extraordinary warhorses. He was surprised by how quick, large, and strong these horses were because the Chinese horses at that time were very small and slow.

He suggested that the emperor could make a lot of money if he traded Chinese silks and other goods for what these distant kingdoms could send to China. Emperor Wudi certainly was interested in getting some of the horses. He sent Zhang with an army to attack Fergana, and after some difficulties, they returned home with many of these animals. On his second trip to Fergana in 106 B.C., Zhang took with him a large quantity of gold and silk. He traded silk for horses. Wudi then decided to enlarge his empire westward.

Today, it is almost impossible for us to imagine how unusual and desired silk was in places far from China, including Rome, during the Han Empire. The Romans used wool and linen, which were rougher and heavier than silk. People were willing to spend large amounts of money for this new material. On the Roman market, it was worth its weight in gold. In much of the ancient world, silk was often used in place of money. However, only the Chinese knew how to make silk, and they guarded that secret carefully. Those working with silk knew that they would be killed if they passed on their knowledge. Although many other goods would travel on these roads, silk was such a valuable item that its name was the one given to the old route. In the nineteenth century, a German geographer Ferdinand von Richthofen called it the Silk Road, and it has had this name ever since.

Besides silk, a great variety of luxury items traveled from east to west and west to east. At its peak, items carried along this road included Byzantine glass from Constantinople (now called Istanbul), Central Asian carpets, slaves, cosmetics, ivory, coral from the Indian Ocean, peonies, ceramic dyes and glazes, and exotic animals such as peacocks, parrots, and ostriches. Unknown vegetables, nuts, and fruits, such as cucumbers, walnuts, peaches, lemons, grapes, figs, and oranges, arrived in China. Only a few merchants traveled the whole way; goods were usually traded along by a series of middlemen. These agents were often based in towns, which developed around **oases**. A single caravan never traveled the whole distance of the route because it was too long. The pack animals–camels, horses, mules, donkeys, bullocks, and yaks–had to be replaced with fresh animals.

It was not only **wares** that journeyed along the Silk Road. The people from different regions and kingdoms who traveled along the route also exchanged ideas, artistic styles, and religious beliefs. Ideas and influences from Greece and Rome as well as from India traveled into Central Asia and eastern China. Monks and **missionaries** carried Buddhism from its Indian birthplace east with the caravans into China. Several important Buddhist civilizations developed in kingdoms along the Silk Road as well as in China.

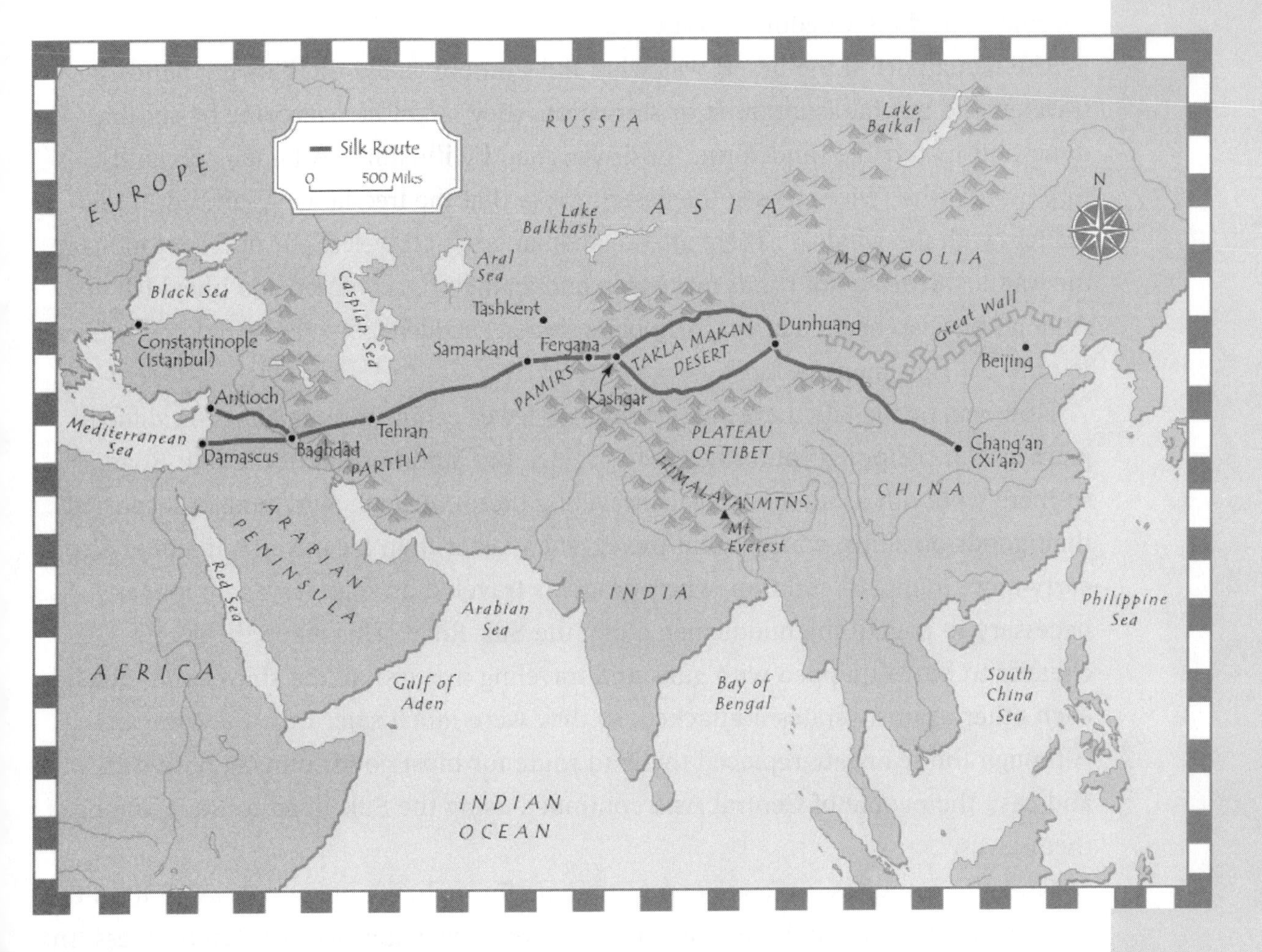

A journey from China on the Silk Road began in Chang'an, which was then the capital. After going west through Dunhuang, the route split into northern and southern branches. This was to avoid the fiercest deserts. Then the two parts rejoined at Kashgar to climb into the mountains of the Pamir, often called the Roof of the World. From there, branches headed south to India and north across the vast plains of Russia, known as the steppe. The main track then moved down across such empires as Persia and Parthia to the shores of the Mediterranean Sea. From there it continued by water to Rome. The land route was more than four thousand miles, much of it through the Takla Makan, one of the most **hostile** deserts in the world. Raiding Huns, Tibetans, and others often attacked travelers along the Silk Road, and the Chinese tried to guard it by building forts and using watchtowers.

What made a trip on the Silk Road possible were the oases that were at the foot of surrounding mountains. They were irrigated by the streams, created from melting glaciers, which flowed down from the mountain ranges that ring the Takla Makan. Without them, the Silk Road could not have existed. Located a few days march from each other, the oases gave travelers a break from the elements as well as from looting **nomads** and bands of murderous robbers who would lie in wait along the way.

As trade increased, these oases became wealthy settlements, and a few of them became important kingdoms for a time.

The worst part of the desert was what the Chinese called the Flowing Sands. If travelers did not die from thirst or starvation, they might be overcome by shifting dunes, hit by terrible sandstorms, or driven mad by **illusions**. A famous seventh-century monk, who twice crossed the desert, wrote that the free-flowing sands drift and scatter "with the wind. . . . There are no landmarks, (so) travelers pile up bones to mark the way. . . . **Searing** hot winds make men and animals . . . confused and [they] fall ill. At times one can hear coughing, or sobbing, but . . . suddenly one does not know where to turn. . . . Thus many perish."

However, by the late thirteenth century, far fewer people were making this difficult journey. New shipping routes began to replace the land portion of the Silk Road, so there were not as many caravans traveling there. Instead, merchants transported their goods on ships, which could travel much faster than a caravan and could also carry more items. In addition, when products traveled by ship, it was no longer necessary to pay all the middlemen along the Silk Road. This made the goods cheaper to buy. Equipped with guns and traveling in a group, the ships could defend each other against pirates if attacked, so they were much safer than the caravans. Although the sea route replaced the land route for most goods moving both west and east, the people of Central Asia continued using the Silk Road to trade among themselves.

Over the centuries, as fewer caravans came through, people moved away from the oasis towns and the mountain kingdoms, looking for better places to do business. In the desert, the sands once again covered the towns. In the mountains, some of the large trading centers were abandoned. In the late nineteenth century, however, Western geographers and mapmakers returned to explore the areas of the East. They discovered old cities in ruins. They found ancient books and other objects buried in the sand or in mountain caves. Once again a fascination with the Silk Road returned. This time the travelers were archaeologists and researchers coming to learn what they could about the trade route and cultural highway that had played a very important part in connecting East and West.

caravan *n.* a company of people traveling together for safety, as through a desert

oasis *n., pl.* **oases** a place in a desert that is fertile because there is water

ware *n.* an article for sale

missionary *n.* a person sent by his or her church to preach and try to persuade other people to join that religion, especially in a foreign country

hostile *adj.* not welcoming, unfriendly

nomad *n.* a person who moves from place to place

illusion *n.* an unreal or misleading appearance or image

searing *adj.* scorching or burning a surface

LOOKING BACK AT WHAT YOU HAVE READ

1. Why do you think some people called Zhang Qian the father of the Silk Road?

____

____

2. Why were many caravans traveling east and west across the Silk Road?

____

____

3. What made the Silk Road so dangerous for travelers?

____

____

4. In order to be successful, what qualities do you think a middleman would have to have?

____

____

5. Why were the oases such an important part of the story of the Silk Road?

____

____

6. Why did silk cost as much as gold in Europe?

____

____

7. When travel on the Silk Road was so dangerous, why do you think people risked their lives to use it?

____

____

8. Besides goods, what else was exchanged along the Silk Road?

____

____

WORKING WITH WORDS

A **metaphor** is a phrase that compares two things that are not alike. It is different from a simile because it does not use the words *like* or *as*. Here are two examples.

When it comes to sports, my brother is *a walking encyclopedia.*

Our car is *a dinosaur*, but we do not miss all the gadgets in the newer ones.

Here are some metaphors describing a journey on the Silk Road. Read them and then draw a picture of what you see in your mind.

The tired travelers were *robots traveling along the winding road.*

The caravan was *an army of ants working its way slowly along.*

To the exhausted travelers the stars were *diamonds glittering in the sky.*

Now imagine you are traveling on the Silk Road. Write a sentence about your journey, using a metaphor.

___

___

You know that **homophones** are words that sound alike but are spelled differently and have different meanings.

Example: *patience* and *patients*

My mother has a lot of *patience*.

There are a lot of *patients* waiting in the doctor's office.

In the first three sentences of the story, there are seven words that are homophones. See if you can find five of them. Write them on the lines below; next to each one write its homophone partner.

______________________ ______________________

______________________ ______________________

______________________ ______________________

______________________ ______________________

______________________ ______________________

______________________ ______________________

______________________ ______________________

An **antonym** is a word that has the opposite meaning of another word. *Generous* is the antonym of *stingy*.

See if you can write two antonyms for each of these words.

impressive ______________________ ______________________

distant ______________________ ______________________

few ______________________ ______________________

valuable ______________________ ______________________

enlarge ______________________ ______________________

enemy ______________________ ______________________

fresh ______________________ ______________________

confuse ______________________ ______________________

WRITING SKILLS

You have been asked to write a short article about the Silk Road for a new history textbook. Think about these questions.

What was the Silk Road?

Where was it?

What was its history?

Why was it important?

Your article will be in paragraph form. Use as many paragraphs as you need. Include details from the story. Be sure that your article has a title and that each paragraph has a topic sentence, which gives the main idea of the paragraph.

First, write down some key ideas. When you have finished your article, proofread it. Does it make sense? Have you included everything you wanted to say? Check it for correct spelling, grammar, capitalization, and punctuation.

Key ideas

- ______________________________
- ______________________________
- ______________________________
- ______________________________

Title:

____

____

____

____

____

____

____

Over the centuries people have written stories about their travel along the Silk Road. Write a paragraph about a trip you have taken. Include many details that will make your reader feel he or she is traveling with you. Be sure that your paragraph has a title, a topic sentence, which gives the main idea of the paragraph, and a concluding sentence, which lets the reader know that you have finished your discussion.

First, write down some key ideas. When you have finished your paragraph, proofread it. Does it make sense? Have you included everything you wanted to say? Check it for correct spelling, grammar, capitalization, and punctuation.

Key ideas

Title:

Birmingham—A BATTLE TO END SEGREGATION

Think about It ....

When you see something unfair happening, what do you do?

____

____

AS YOU READ Put a ★ beside each important idea in the story. Then write in the margin why each is important. Put a ✓ next to parts of the story that you find interesting. Put a **?** next to parts of the story you do not understand.

OTES

For years, civil rights leaders had fought to end segregation in the South, but progress was slow. By 1962, they believed that tensions between African Americans and whites would have to reach a boiling point for any change to take place. As one civil rights leader said, "We've got to have a crisis to bargain with." The Southern Christian Leadership Conference (SCLC), headed by Martin Luther King Jr., decided to create such a crisis. The SCLC planned a campaign against segregation in Birmingham, Alabama, to end separate treatment of African Americans at lunch counters, at water fountains, and in hiring for jobs.

Birmingham was known as the most segregated city in the country. Violence was often present. There had been so many bombings in African-American neighborhoods that the city was nicknamed "Bombingham." Even though Birmingham had thriving steel mills, African Americans were hired only for unskilled jobs. Nowhere in the city could African Americans use water fountains, rest rooms, dressing rooms, parks, or any other place marked "For Whites Only." Although **sit-ins** at lunch counters had succeeded in changing segregation laws in other cities, Birmingham's lunch counters were still segregated.

The SCLC decided to end segregation in Birmingham in stages. First, they would have small sit-ins at some lunch counters with protesters carrying signs outside the businesses, and they would hold nightly **mass** meetings. Next, the SCLC would organize a

boycott of Birmingham's downtown stores and have larger demonstrations. Finally, they would start mass marches to the downtown that would **enforce** the boycott. Large numbers of protesters would willingly be arrested in order to fill up Birmingham's jails. The SCLC hoped that the boycott, the overflowing jails, and the attention from newspapers and television would so cripple the city that the mayor would be forced to talk with the SCLC to end segregation. Using the Sixteenth Street Baptist Church as a headquarters, the SCLC taught 250 African-American city residents how to protest in a nonviolent way. Then these people went to other African-American churches in the city to teach this method to others.

The first small sit-ins and the marches began on Wednesday, April 3, 1963. Although protesters were arrested, there was no violence. Eight days after the campaign began, Martin Luther King Jr. received an order from the state court, which forbade him and other SCLC leaders from taking part in any more demonstrations. King said he would not follow the order because it was a "pseudo" or fake law. He told reporters that he was willing to go to jail with everyone else. "Here in Birmingham, we have reached the point of no return." Soon after, King was arrested and jailed for nine days.

When King was freed on **bail**, he learned that the demonstrations had weakened. One civil rights leader recalled, "We needed more troops. We had scraped the bottom of the barrel of adults who would go to jail." This was because the adults needed to hold their jobs so that they could take care of their families. James Bevel, one of the SCLC leaders, suggested signing up high school students, and King agreed. "We needed this dramatic new dimension," he later said. Soon teenagers were crowding into the churches to attend the nonviolent workshops. Every day younger, uninvited brothers and sisters came, too, ready to march to jail. Their parents, as well as many African-American leaders, did not like the idea of putting young children in such a dangerous position, but King decided that the children would march, saying no one was too young to protest segregation.

On April 30, after the city refused to give the SCLC a parade permit, the group announced there would be a huge march of high school students on Thursday, May 2, with or without a permit. Throughout Birmingham's African-American high schools and elementary schools, news of the upcoming march spread. Over the radio, a popular rock-and-roll disc jockey announced that there would be a "big party" on Thursday.

On May 2, shortly after one o'clock, the front doors of the Sixteenth Street Baptist Church opened, and fifty teenagers came out, walking two by two, singing "We Shall Overcome" and clapping. Quickly, police officers started directing the teenagers into police vans. It seemed like just another day in the month-long protest, but then a second double line of marchers came out of the church, then another, and another, filling the streets. The police commissioner ordered all of them locked up. But doing this was not easy. The young protesters had tricks to distract the police. With lines of marchers acting as **decoys** heading one way, large groups of picketers were able to move through the police lines and proceed to the downtown stores. When a tough-looking police captain tried to convince a group of thirty-eight elementary school students to leave the lines of marchers, they refused, telling him they knew what they were doing. One little girl, who was asked her age as she climbed into a police van, called out that she was six. Fighting for their freedom, over nine hundred children went to jail on May 2.

The following day, anxious parents and onlookers jammed into a park directly across from the Sixteenth Street Baptist Church. Inside, another group of young people, now more than a thousand, received their orders. This time the police blocked the church, and firefighters, who had been called up by the police commissioner, stood ready with hoses. They had set the water pressure in the hoses to be so great that it could peel bark from a tree. When people tried to leave the building, the firefighters blasted both adults and children. The jet streams ripped their clothes and left them bloodied on the ground. The police swung nightsticks and set police dogs loose among the panicked crowd.

During the next few days, angered by the continuing cruelty of the police, some of the demonstrators abandoned their discipline and started throwing bottles and bricks at the police. The police became more vicious. Many Birmingham whites started to fear an actual war between whites and African Americans. Because of the boycotts and the disorder, people did not go to the downtown stores. Businessmen saw their sales and profits drop. President Kennedy sent representatives to meet with the Birmingham businessmen, telling them they had to reach an agreement with the SCLC. The businessmen said this was impossible and ended the meeting. When they went outside, however, "there were square blocks of Negroes on the sidewalks, in the streets, standing, sitting in the aisles of downtown stores. Downtown Birmingham echoed to the strains of the freedom songs." President Kennedy continued to telephone important business leaders, arguing for a settlement. Three days later, the businessmen and the SCLC reached an informal **pact**. In exchange for an immediate stop to the protests, the business owners would meet all demands for ending segregation and for hiring African Americans during the next three months.

But people on both sides were furious with the plan. African Americans said that King had traded their protest weapon for promises, and some whites, including Governor George Wallace of Alabama, rejected any settlement. Two dynamite explosions destroyed the home of King's brother, a Birmingham minister, and blew out part of the motel where King and his aides were staying. Angry because of these attacks, African Americans threw rocks at police, and some state troopers began beating African Americans. On the streets, King spoke against violence, but the agreement with the business leaders seemed about to collapse.

However, Americans were sickened when they saw on their television sets and in photos on the front pages of newspapers the brutal treatment of African Americans by the police. President Kennedy warned that he would not have **extremists** weaken the settlement, which, he said, was fair and just. On May 12, 1963, the president ordered three thousand army troops to gather near Birmingham. Finally, the agreement was approved. Birmingham's merchants opened lunch counters, water fountains, and rest rooms to all people, and African Americans were hired for jobs that before were only open to whites. Albert Boutwell, the city's new mayor, canceled the city's segregation laws. Sadly, there would be more bloodshed and violence before the Civil Rights Act of 1964 was passed, allowing the United States government to enforce these new laws in every state in the Union.

sit-in *n.* a way to protest without using violence, in which people purposely sit down in places where segregation laws say they cannot sit

mass *adj.* involving or attended by large numbers of people

boycott *n.* the refusal as part of an organized group to use, buy from, or deal with a store, company, person, or nation

enforce *v.* to carry out the law

bail *n.* money that is given so that a prisoner can be let out of jail until his or her trial takes place

decoy *n.* a person or thing that is used to lead others into danger or a trap

pact *n.* an agreement between people or countries to do certain things

extremist *n.* a person with views that are far from the usual views people have, especially in politics or religion

LOOKING BACK AT WHAT YOU HAVE READ

On the lines under each of the three boxes, write details from the story that give information about these topics.

Birmingham – A Battle to End Segregation

SCLC's Plan to End Segregation	Role of Teenagers and Children	Results of Protests
____________	____________	____________
____________	____________	____________
____________	____________	____________
____________	____________	____________
____________	____________	____________
____________	____________	____________
____________	____________	____________
____________	____________	____________

WORKING WITH WORDS

A **proverb** is a common saying that expresses something that many people believe to be true. "Actions speak louder than words" is a proverb. It means that what a person does is more important than what she or he says.

Explain how the Birmingham protest is an example of the proverb "Where there is a will, there is a way."

____

____

____

Explain how the actions of the Birmingham police are an example of the proverb "A picture is worth a thousand words."

____

____

____

You remember that a **synonym** is a word that has the same or almost the same meaning as another word. *Happy* and *cheerful* are synonyms. An **antonym** is a word that has the opposite meaning of another word. *Funny* and *sad* are antonyms.

Give a synonym and an antonym for each word.

	synonym	**antonym**
thriving	____________	____________
cruelty	____________	____________
hired	____________	____________
forbade	____________	____________

	synonym	antonym
reject	________________	________________
swift	________________	________________
recall	________________	________________

Look at the following phrases from the story. On the lines, write a sentence using each of the words in bold print.

Example:

abandoned their discipline

When it started to pour, we abandoned our campsite and went to a motel.

to have a **crisis**

____

____

dramatic new dimensions

____

____

a dangerous **position**

____

____

progress was slow

____

____

would **cripple** the city

____

____

to **distract** the police

____

____

jammed into a park

____

____

WRITING SKILLS

An **expanded paragraph** is one in which you use several supporting ideas to develop your main idea. To make your meaning clear, you should use **transition words**. These words give the signal that you have finished discussing one supporting idea and are ready to move to the next. Remember that these words are always followed by a comma. Here are some common transition words.

first second next last finally

African Americans had mixed feelings about using children in Birmingham's battle to end segregation. Imagine that you are a father or a mother of a child who wants to participate in the protest.

Write an expanded paragraph supporting your child's decision to participate in the protests. Make sure you give specific reasons. Try to use at least three of the transition words above. Be sure your paragraph has a title, a topic sentence, which gives the main idea of the paragraph, and a concluding sentence, which lets the reader know that you have finished your discussion.

First, write down some key ideas. When you have finished your paragraph, proofread your writing. Does it make sense? Have you included everything you wanted to say? Check for correct spelling, grammar, capitalization, and punctuation.

Key ideas

- ______________________________
- ______________________________
- ______________________________
- ______________________________

Title:

____

____

____

____

Now write an expanded paragraph explaining why you refuse to let your child participate in the protests. Again, make sure you include specific reasons. Try to use at least three of the transition words above. Be sure your paragraph has a title, a topic sentence, which gives the main idea of the paragraph, and a concluding sentence, which lets the reader know that you have finished your discussion.

First, write down some key ideas. When you have finished your paragraph, proofread your writing. Does it make sense? Have you included everything you wanted to say? Check for correct spelling, grammar, capitalization, and punctuation.

Key ideas

Title:

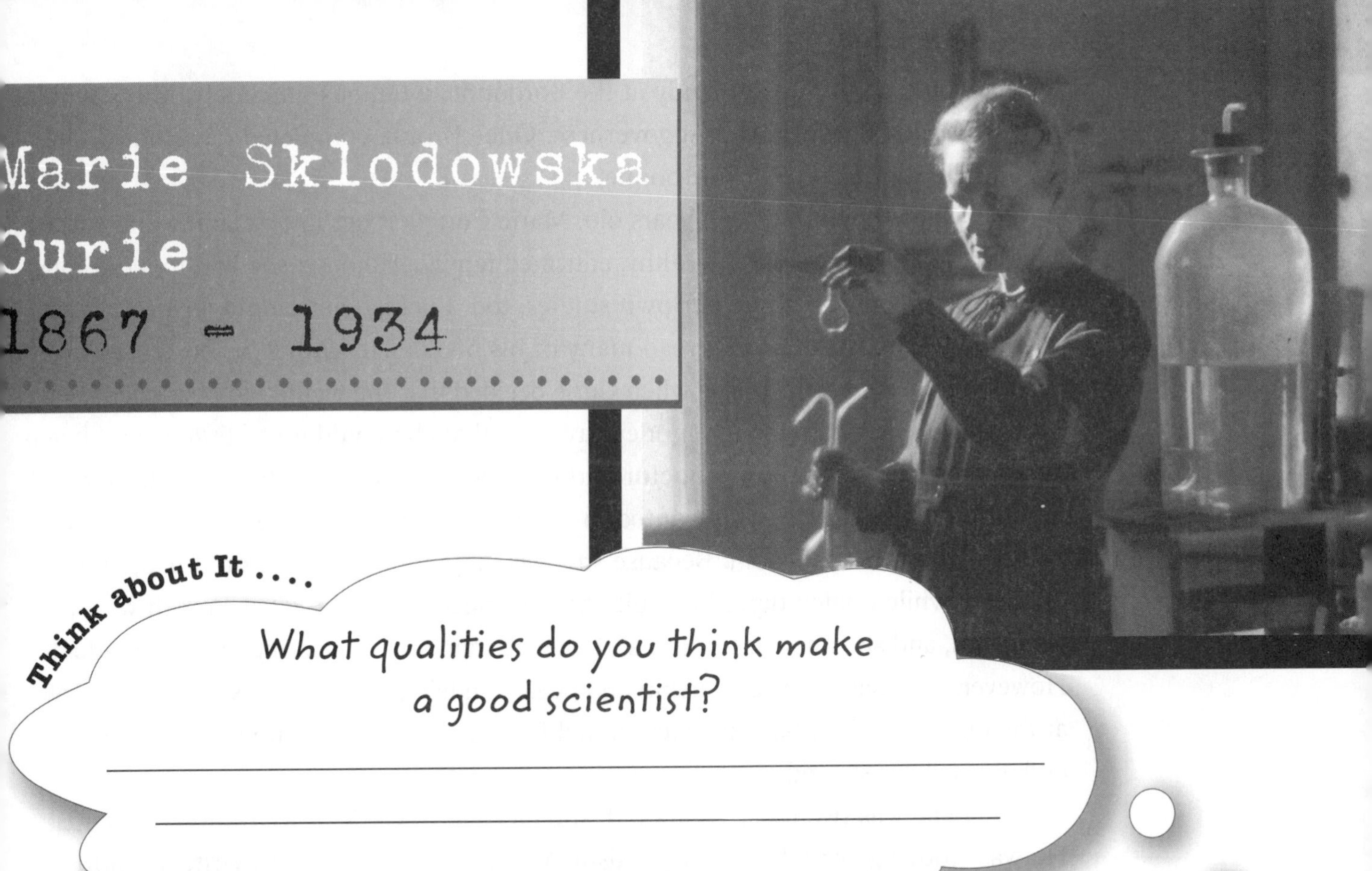

AS YOU READ Put a ★ beside each important idea in the story. Then write in the margin why each is important. Put a ✓ next to parts of the story that you find interesting. Put a **?** next to parts of the story you do not understand.

NOTES

In the late 1890s, Marie Curie, a young scientist, became very excited about a new field, the study of invisible rays. Unlike rays of light, these rays could not be seen or explained. She and her husband Pierre identified two new **elements**, polonium and radium, which gave off these rays. For their work, the Curies and Henri Becquerel, a French physicist who discovered natural **radioactivity**, received the 1903 Nobel Prize in physics. After her husband died in an accident, Marie Curie continued their work, determining that radioactivity comes from within the atoms. Her discoveries would unlock the secrets of radioactivity and lead not only to the first cancer treatment using **radiation** but also to the use of nuclear energy.

Curie came from a very close-knit family. Her parents were both educators. Her mother was the principal of a school and her father taught physics and math at a high school. Marie was the youngest of five children. Unfortunately, an older sister died when Marie was nine, and two years later her mother died. She was only fifteen years old when she graduated from high school in Warsaw, Poland. Even though she was the youngest in her class, she was the best student in every subject. Curie wanted to go to college, but in those days Warsaw University did not accept women students. To attend college, she would have to go to another country. So Marie and her older sister Bronia, who wanted to be a doctor, thought of a plan that in time would give them both a college degree. First,

Bronia would go to Paris to study at the Sorbonne, a famous university. Marie would support Bronia by working as a governess. Once Bronia completed her studies, she would help Marie go to the Sorbonne.

When she was just eighteen years old, Marie Curie left her loving family and started working as a governess for a wealthy, educated family. Although she had to work long hours, she tried to continue her own studies, too. Luckily, her **employer** had a large scientific library, so she could read many of his books. Her father, in his letters to her, tutored her in math. This is when Curie decided that she wanted to be a scientist.

In 1891, Curie had enough money saved so that she could go to France and begin her studies. Her sister, now a doctor and married, invited Marie to stay with her and her husband. But Curie, who wanted to be free to work as she pleased, decided to rent a sixth-floor attic room. Because she was very poor, she lived on bread, and once in a while treated herself to fruit and hot chocolate. At first, her French was not very good, and she knew less math and science than any French high school graduate. However, she received a scholarship and began studying math, physics, and chemistry at the university. In 1893, she was ranked first on the French state exams in physics and a year later second on the exams in mathematics.

When she was twenty-six years old, she met Pierre Curie, a well-known scientist. He was studying crystals and magnetism. Marie had been asked to write a report about the magnetic properties of different kinds of steel. In fact, their **mutual** interest in magnetism drew them together. Both were deeply interested in science and both loved their work. A year and a half after their first meeting, the two were married.

Marie Curie wanted to work in a new field of science. She wished to explore an area so new that no books had yet been written about it. In 1896, physicist Henri Becquerel had discovered that uranium sent out radiation that strongly resembled X rays. These powerful rays could pass through substances that ordinary rays of light could not go through. Becquerel was able to show that this radiation was not dependent on an outside source of energy but seemed to come from the uranium itself. Marie Curie had a **hunch** that other substances might send out this radiation, too. She decided to concentrate her research on uranium ore, which is called pitchblende. She knew that the uranium in the pitchblende was radioactive, but the pitchblende was giving off much more radiation than could be traced to the amounts of uranium in it. Curie thought that the pitchblende might hold one or more unknown elements and that they were the source of the additional radiation. She wanted to prove this.

Soon Pierre Curie was attracted to his wife's work, and the project quickly became his work as much as hers. Using a method of chemical research, the Curies identified two new elements, which were highly radioactive. One they called polonium; the second, more active element, they called radium. By the end of 1898, Marie and Pierre Curie announced their discovery.

Both of them were convinced that radium and polonium existed. But Marie Curie knew that if she wanted other chemists to admit the existence of these two new elements, she would have to **isolate** larger quantities from the pitchblende. There was only one problem. She would need tons of pitchblende, which would be very expensive. The

Curies came up with a simple but brilliant idea. The uranium ore in pitchblende was used in the manufacture of glass. When the ore was mined, the uranium was separated from the rest of the pitchblende and what remained was discarded. Why couldn't the undiscovered elements be found in these remains? In 1898, the directors of a mine in Bohemia (then part of Austria, now part of the Czech Republic) were willing to sell the leftover pitchblende to the Curies at a reasonable price. In the same year, in a simple brick-walled shed at the School of Physics where her husband taught, Marie Curie began her work.

She knew she would have to crush and boil down tons of the pitchblende remains in order to concentrate and isolate just one tenth of a gram of radium and polonium. She wrote, "It was exhausting work to move the containers about, to transfer the liquid, and to stir for hours at a time, with an iron bar, the boiling material in the cast-iron basin." Later, Pierre Curie said he never would have taken on the job of isolating radium. But Marie Curie was not afraid of this exhausting physical labor. She was determined to succeed.

In 1903, Marie and Pierre Curie shared the Nobel Prize in physics with Henri Becquerel for their discoveries related to radioactivity. Late in 1904, a month before the birth of their second daughter, Marie Curie was finally offered a position as her husband's assistant at the Sorbonne, where she had been working without pay for years. Marie Curie was very pleased. Then on a rainy afternoon in 1906, her happy life changed completely. As Pierre Curie was crossing a busy Paris street after a meeting with other professors, he was run over by a horse-drawn wagon and killed instantly.

Marie Curie was heartbroken, but she was determined to continue her work in science. The Sorbonne asked her to take over her husband's job as a physics professor. When she agreed to do this, she became the first woman professor in the Sorbonne's 650-year-old history and the first woman professor in France. Curie continued her work with radium, and in 1910, twelve years after she began, she announced that she had isolated pure radium. A year later, for this work and her studies of radium's chemistry, she was awarded the Nobel Prize in chemistry.

During World War I, Curie helped the French army. Many French army doctors did not think X rays were necessary. Even though her work had never dealt with these rays, she knew what a basic tool they were. She created training courses in the use of X rays for medical orderlies, and she taught doctors how to use them to locate foreign objects such as rifle bullets and other pieces of metal in the body. With this information, they could operate more quickly and accurately. Curie raised money to equip several cars with portable X-ray machines. She then accompanied one of them to the front lines. Because of her work, more then a million X rays were taken.

After the war was over, she helped found the Radium Institute in Paris where scientists could study radioactivity. Later, the name was changed to the Curie Institute. She spent the rest of her life exploring the properties of radioactive substances. Unfortunately, her death in July 1934 was probably hastened by her exposure to radiation. Not knowing how dangerous it was, Marie Curie had been exposed to more radiation than any other human being.

element *n.* one of over one hundred basic substances that each has its own kind of atom and cannot be broken down into any simpler form by ordinary chemical means

radioactivity *n.* the process by which certain chemical elements, such as radium, give off energy in the form of rays or waves

radiation *n.* the act or process of giving off energy in the form of rays or waves

employer *n.* a person or business that hires people for wages or a salary

mutual *adj.* shared; given and received equally

hunch *n.* a strong feeling, without any reason for it, especially about some future event

isolate *v.* to separate from another substance in order to obtain a pure form of something

LOOKING BACK AT WHAT YOU HAVE READ

1. How do we know that Marie Curie was a very determined person?

____

____

2. How did her family help Marie Curie?

____

____

3. Why did Marie Curie go to college in France?

____

____

4. How did the Curies work as a team?

____

____

5. What two elements did Marie Curie discover?

____

____

6. Was Marie Curie a practical person? Explain your answer.

7. How did Henri Becquerel influence Marie Curie's life?

8. Why do you think that Marie Curie was such a successful scientist? Explain your answer.

WORKING WITH WORDS

You know that a **definition** explains the meaning of a word or group of words. A definition of the word *hobby* is something done regularly in one's spare time for pleasure.

Write a definition for the following words:

determined

attract

accompany

support

governess

Before Marie Curie could isolate radium and establish a way of removing radium from pitchblende, she had to work extremely hard. Think of a time when you had to work very hard. When was it? Write this down, and then write down as many **adjectives** as you can think of that describe how you felt. Try to think of at least five.

____

____

____________ ____________ ____________

____________ ____________ ____________

____________ ____________

Some words are spelled alike but have different meanings. These words are called **homographs**.

Example: A *pupil* can mean a person who is studying in school or with a teacher. It can also mean the opening in the center of the eye.

See if you can fill in the correct homograph for each group of sentences.

Marie Curie was very____________.

The full moon is very ____________.

Curie was so busy that she rarely had time to ____________.

May I have the ____________ of the ice cream?

I wonder if there were ____________ in the Curie laboratory?

A fish is covered with ____________.

It was a great ____________ to Marie Curie when her husband was killed.

The little girl asked her mother to ____________ up her balloon.

When Curie became famous, she was often asked to be a ________________ in many different places.

Does your stereo have a big ________________?

The enthusiastic crowd ________________ to greet Marie Curie.

The ________________ smells very nice.

Who would pay the ________________ for the X-ray machines?

A bird's ________________ is very hard.

Curie was pleased when she received a ________________ so that she could equip an ambulance.

Please ________________ to see if the baby is sleeping.

I have to ________________ my homework before I hand it in.

WRITING SKILLS

Marie Curie equipped ambulances with X-ray machines during World War I. To do this she needed money, so she asked people for donations. Pretend you are Marie Curie and write an article for a newspaper describing your work and asking the readers for money to buy the ambulances and the X-ray machines.

Your article will be in paragraph form. Use as many paragraphs as you need. What will you include in your article? Use details from the story. Be sure that your article has a title and that each paragraph has a topic sentence, which gives the main idea of the paragraph.

First, write down some key ideas. When you have finished your article, proofread it. Does it make sense? Have you included everything you wanted to say? Check it for correct spelling, grammar, capitalization, and punctuation.

Key ideas

____

____

____

____

Title:

When a famous person dies, an obituary, a printed notice of the death with a biography, is in the newspaper. Pretend you work for a newspaper; you are asked to write Marie Curie's obituary. Be sure to answer the following questions:

Who was she?

When did she live and die?

Where did she live?

What did she do?

First, write down some key ideas. When you have finished your obituary, proofread it. Does it make sense? Have you included everything you wanted to say? Check it for correct spelling, grammar, capitalization, and punctuation.

Key ideas

Obituary:

AS YOU READ Put a ★ beside each important idea in the story. Then write in the margin why each is important. Put a ✓ next to parts of the story that you find interesting. Put a ? next to parts of the story you do not understand.

OTES

Easter Island, also known as Rapa Nui, is a small island that has many volcanic craters. It is about 2,300 miles off the coast of Chile, a country in South America. The island has fascinated people for hundreds of years because of its many mysterious, gigantic stone statues, or moai. The island was first noticed by the outside world in 1722 when Jacob Roggeveen, a Dutch explorer, spotted it from his ship. Because he discovered it on Easter Sunday, Roggeveen named it Easter Island. A couple of days later he made a short visit to the island. Writing in his journal, Roggeveen said, "Concerning the religion of these people, of this we could get no full knowledge because of the shortness of our stay; we merely observed they set fires before some particularly high erected stone images. . . . these stone images at first caused us to be struck with astonishment, because we could not comprehend how it was possible that these people, who are **devoid** of heavy thick timber for making any machines, as well as strong ropes, nevertheless had been able to erect such images, which were fully thirty feet high and thick in proportion."

We do not know exactly when the first settlers came to Easter Island. Some researchers think they arrived about A.D. 690, but others suggest they may have arrived as early as A.D. 400. Experts now believe that these settlers came from the islands of

Polynesia. It is said that Hotu Matua, a powerful Polynesian chief, settled the island, arriving with a group of colonists in two large sailing canoes. Whoever these first people were, researchers believe that they had no contact with other people for over a thousand years, but they still prospered. Their population grew and may have reached ten thousand people. When twentieth-century explorers came to the island, they found no written history. There were a few wooden tablets carved with symbols that no one understands and a few spoken stories that have been passed down within families. What they did find were large stone platforms and huge broken statues.

Over the years, using blocks of volcanic stone, the islanders built long, narrow, raised platforms, called ahus. Some of these were quite low while others were up to ten feet high. Between 250 and 300 ahus are on the island, and of these about 125 had statues on them. To make some of these platforms, stones weighing from three hundred to five hundred tons had to be moved. The ahus form an almost unbroken line around the island's coast, with distinct clusters around **coves**, which made good landing places and which were areas with good living conditions. Placed as close to the shore as possible and parallel to it, they form impressive walls, which seem to rise straight out of the sea. On the side facing the land, the platform had a ramp, which sloped down to a flat open area. Researchers believe that the ahus marked boundaries and served as centers of some kind for the people. From time to time, statues made from different kinds of rock were placed near these ahus.

Great teamwork must have been necessary to split the enormous chunks of stone from the **quarries**, located in different parts of the island. Then, the stones needed to be squared with stone **picks**, dragged on rollers or sleds over rough ground for many miles, and then fitted exactly into place. Hundreds of people must have worked for months on each project. Archaeologists believe that over the years the ahus gradually got larger as the statues became much larger. Although a few platforms seem to have been built just to hold burials, the usual ahu appears to have had many uses. It served as a place to meet and to hold ceremonies as well as a place that represented one's family or marked a boundary. The building of platforms seems to have become an **obsession** by about A.D. 1200, and this "golden age," the peak construction time for both platforms and statues, lasted well into the sixteenth century.

The most amazing cultural achievement of the Easter Islanders was the production of hundreds of gigantic stone statues without the use of metal tools. These statues are similar in style and are unique to Easter Island. Most of the statues are neither male nor female. More than 230 of the statues were erected on ahus. Each of the platforms might carry from one to fifteen statues in a row, with no two figures exactly alike in height, width, or weight. Despite differences in form and size, the figures have tall heads with full-length torsos ending in flat, flaring bases without legs. The arms are long and slender with hands bent and fingers close together on each side. The small mouths of these stone figures are wrinkled. Some statues have huge red stone cylinders balanced on their heads like hats, which researchers have named topknots. Some think that these stand for the headdresses worn by the chiefs. About nine hundred of these statues were made, usually measuring from eleven to twenty-five feet in height. The largest statue placed on an ahu measures thirty-two feet, weighs about 50 tons, and once carried a topknot, weighing 10 tons. An unfinished statue still attached to the quarry wall and nicknamed "El Gigante" measures sixty-five feet long, which is equal to the height of a seven-story building, and weighs around 270 tons.

Some archaeologists believe that every family group on the island built statues to honor their **ancestors**. A statue would serve as a person's funeral monument and would keep the dead person's memory alive. A platform might have up to fifteen statues on it. The islanders may have thought that these figures had supernatural powers that would help their community. When the builders made the statues, they added the eyes last, after placing the statue on the ahu. It is possible that they believed that adding the eyes to the statue as the last detail gave it supernatural power, which allowed it to talk with the islanders' ancestors. Other archaeologists believe that the statues represented important family members. The statue would be ordered during the lifetime of the important person, just as the pharaohs of Egypt ordered their pyramids. Since the person was still alive when the statue was made, the eye sockets were left empty, showing that the person was still living. However, when the family member died and the statue was moved to the ahu, then the eyes would be set in place. In addition, a headdress might be placed on the statue. As the years passed, the islanders made their statues larger.

Experts believe that it took a team of twenty people about a year to carve one of the largest statues and remove it from the quarry wall. What makes this work even more amazing is that the statues were moved after the details of their carving were completed in the quarry. To move them without damaging them must have been a very difficult task.

No one knows how these statues were moved and placed on the platforms. Island tradition says that the priests had a special power that caused the statues to walk a short distance each day until they finally reached the ahu. Researchers think that perhaps many people pulled the statue over the ground on some sort of large sled or laid down a track of tree trunks over which they dragged the statue. Such teamwork would have been possible only during a time of peace and plenty. It is likely that different methods for moving the statues were developed over the centuries. Depending on the size of each, they were rolled, pulled, or rocked into place.

For some reason, during the second half of the 1700s, all work on the statues stopped. Visitors to the island see proof of this even today. At the quarry, tools have been left as though ready for another day of work. More than eighty statues are still there, unfinished. Statues in the process of being moved to ahus were simply left lying on the road. In 1770, when a Spanish ship visited the island, some of the gigantic human statues were still standing. Just four years later, however, when the Englishman Captain James Cook made a brief, unplanned stop at the island, he reported that many statues had been overturned next to their platforms, and that the monuments were no longer cared for. Between 1722, when the Dutch believed that the statue obsession was still going strong, and 1774, when Cook thought the statues were finished, something drastic had happened.

For many years people have wondered, what terrible thing could have occurred? Perhaps groups who earlier had competed with each other through the size and magnificence of their statues, turned to fighting each other. Whoever won the battle may have taken revenge by toppling and damaging the other group's statues to further shame them. The mystery of what really happened remains. Yet the Easter Island statues continue to fascinate people. Nothing quite like them exists anywhere else.

devoid *adj.* completely lacking

cove *n.* a small, sheltered bay or inlet

quarry *n.* a place where stone is cut or blasted out

pick *n.* a tool with a wooden handle and a metal head that is pointed at one or both ends and is used for breaking rock and loosening dirt

obsession *n.* an idea, a thought, or an emotion that occupies the mind continually

ancestor *n.* a person from whom one is descended

LOOKING BACK AT WHAT YOU HAVE READ

1. Where is Easter Island?

____

____

2. Why do people think that Easter Island is a remarkable place?

____

____

3. What was an ahu for and how was it built?

____

____

4. Why were stone statues built on Easter Island?

____

____

5. How do you think the people of Easter Island were able to move these heavy statues and put them in place?

____

____

6. What do you think drove the islanders to work so hard on the statues?

____

____

7. Why did the islanders add the eyes to the statues last?

____

____

8. How do we know that the work on the statues stopped suddenly?

____

____

WORKING WITH WORDS

The statues on Easter Island are very large. Think of words that mean the same or nearly the same as *large.* Make a list. Then make a word line by arranging them in a sequence to show degrees of largeness.

Example: tiny

List: little wee minute tiny petite miniature small

Word line: small little petite tiny miniature wee minute

large

List: ____

Word line: ____

In an **analogy**, you are trying to figure out the connection between two pairs of words.

Example: Stove is to cooking as desk is to ________.

First, you must understand the connection between the words in the first pair, stove/cooking. Make a picture in your mind of these words. Think how they are related. Then make a sentence describing what you see.

A stove *is used for* cooking.

Now use the word or words you have pictured to make the same connection between the second pair of words. What is a desk used for?

A desk *is used for* writing.

The analogy, then, is stove is to cooking as desk is to writing.

In the following analogies, decide what the connection is between the first pair of words. Make a picture of these words in your mind. Think how they are related. Next, write a word in the blank that will show the same connection between the second pair of words.

Jacob Roggeveen is to explorer as Ludwig van Beethoven is to ________.

Polynesia is to island as California is to ________.

Canoe is to boat as lamb chop is to ________.

Unique is to unusual as slender is to ________.

El Gigante is to statue as Mount Rainier is to ________.

An ahu is to stone as a dress is to ________.

An **idiom** is a group of words that have a special meaning. If you do not know the special meaning, you will not understand what a person is saying. It may even sound ridiculous.
For example, "To get into someone's hair." This means you are annoying someone.

Read the explanations of the following idioms. Then write a sentence using the idiom.

The idiom "keep plugging away" means that a person keeps on trying no matter how difficult the job is.

Even though it was difficult to move a statue, the Easter Islanders kept plugging away.

The idiom "up a tree" means in trouble.
Even though there was great teamwork, sometimes the workers constructing an ahu must have felt they were up a tree.

The idiom "batting a thousand" means you have done a perfect job.
When a statue was finally successfully placed on an ahu, the workers probably felt they were batting a thousand.

You have been asked to write a page about Easter Island for a book about unsolved mysteries of the world. What will you include in your description? Use details from the story. Of course, your description will have a topic sentence, which gives the main idea of the paragraph, and a concluding sentence, which lets the reader know that you have finished your discussion.

First, write down some key ideas. When you have finished the paragraph, proofread your writing. Does it make sense? Have you included everything you wanted to say? Check it for correct spelling, grammar, capitalization, and punctuation.

Key ideas

THE UNSOLVED MYSTERY OF EASTER ISLAND

There are wonderful stories about people who were shipwrecked on a deserted island. Easter Island was not always deserted, but it certainly must have been very different from other places. What do you think it would be like to be a sailor shipwrecked on Easter Island at the time the statues were being built? Write a four-paragraph composition describing your adventure. Be sure to include a title. Think about what life is like for you on the island and about how you are rescued.

Put your supporting ideas into separate paragraphs. Make certain that each supporting paragraph has its own topic sentence. You will need one paragraph each for your introduction and conclusion.

First, write an outline for your composition. When you have finished your composition, proofread your writing. Does it make sense? Have you included everything you wanted to say? Check it for correct spelling, grammar, capitalization, and punctuation.

Outline

Introduction

Paragraph 1

Paragraph 2

Conclusion

Title:

The Capture of QUEBEC

Think about It ....

What is a time when your careful planning paid off for you?

____

____

AS YOU READ Put a ★ beside each important idea in the story. Then write in the margin why each is important. Put a ✓ next to parts of the story that you find interesting. Put a **?** next to parts of the story you do not understand.

NOTES

In 1759, Britain and France were at war, both in Europe and in North America. William Pitt, Britain's secretary for war, declared that all French colonies must be conquered and all French trade overseas stopped. As part of Pitt's plan, in June 1759, a British fleet of 140 ships, the largest ever sent to America, sailed on the Saint Lawrence River to Quebec, a French fortress and town. Aboard the ships was a large army under the command of the **accomplished** young general James Wolfe. His orders were simple–capture Quebec.

Wolfe's first view of Quebec revealed a huge fortress built on top of the steep cliffs rising straight up from the river. He knew it was surrounded by enormous **fortifications**. Between the fortress and the fortifications was a town. The high cliffs along the Saint Lawrence River protected the south side of Quebec. On the north and west, it was protected by the Saint Charles River and by a deep, narrow gorge. Wolfe realized how difficult it would be to lead his army up the cliffs. He placed part of his troops near the gorge, just east of the fortifications, part on the Island of Orleans, five miles beyond Quebec, and the rest on the opposite shore of the Saint Lawrence River, facing Quebec.

Guarding Quebec was the brilliant French general Louis Joseph de Montcalm. The last orders he had received from France commanded him to keep a **foothold** in America whatever the cost. Montcalm had replied, "I shall do everything to **maintain** it, or die." He knew that he did not have the troops to attack and defeat Wolfe. His French army was not even half the size of Wolfe's. Although he had gathered together ten thousand **militia** and some Native Americans, they were not experienced soldiers. He knew that as the season advanced the militia would probably return to their farms to gather the harvest. He also noticed that the Native Americans were showing signs of turning to the enemy because they thought that the British would win the war.

There were no French naval ships nearby to support him. Yet, he did everything he could to defend Quebec. He repaired the walls of the fortress and put cannons on floats on the Saint Lawrence River, close to the land. Montcalm's aim was clear: he was determined to hold Quebec until the fall storms began and the river froze. He knew that the ice would crush Wolfe's wooden ships. Without the ships, Wolfe would not be able to bring food in for his army. The beginning of winter weather would force Wolfe to withdraw his troops from Quebec.

Montcalm, however, had another problem to consider. The Governor of New France, Pierre Vaudreuil de Cavagnal, was jealous of Montcalm and opposed many of his requests and orders. This made it very difficult for Montcalm to organize his troops to defend Quebec against the British. Vaudreuil claimed that he was the head of the French forces in the colony and, therefore, he had the right to direct the militia. He even canceled Montcalm's orders to the French soldiers. Before the English fleet arrived right below Quebec, Montcalm had sent troops to hold Point Levi, a piece of land directly across the river from Quebec. But Vaudreuil ordered the soldiers to return to the city, so this important post was left open to the enemy. Soon the British were using it regularly to bombard Quebec.

As the summer passed, Wolfe destroyed many villages that supplied food to Quebec and fired on the town and fortifications from the ships, but he could not take Quebec. Montcalm, or the "old fox" as Wolfe called him, had stopped every attack.

The French depended on food brought in ships on the Saint Lawrence River. Because the British ships were stationed right across from Quebec, the only way to get food to the town was to slip barges by the ships at night. They landed in a cove two miles beyond Quebec and the British ships. There, using a steep path up the cliffs, people carried supplies up to the fortress.

Near the end of the summer, Wolfe discovered the cove. On one of his scouting trips up and down the river, he noticed women doing laundry by the river near Quebec. In those days, armies usually included women for this purpose. When Wolfe saw the washing hung out to dry at the top of the cliff a short time later, he realized that there must be a path from the edge of the river to the level above. Through a deserter from the French camp, the British learned that this was true.

By early September, Wolfe decided he would try to capture the fortress before the

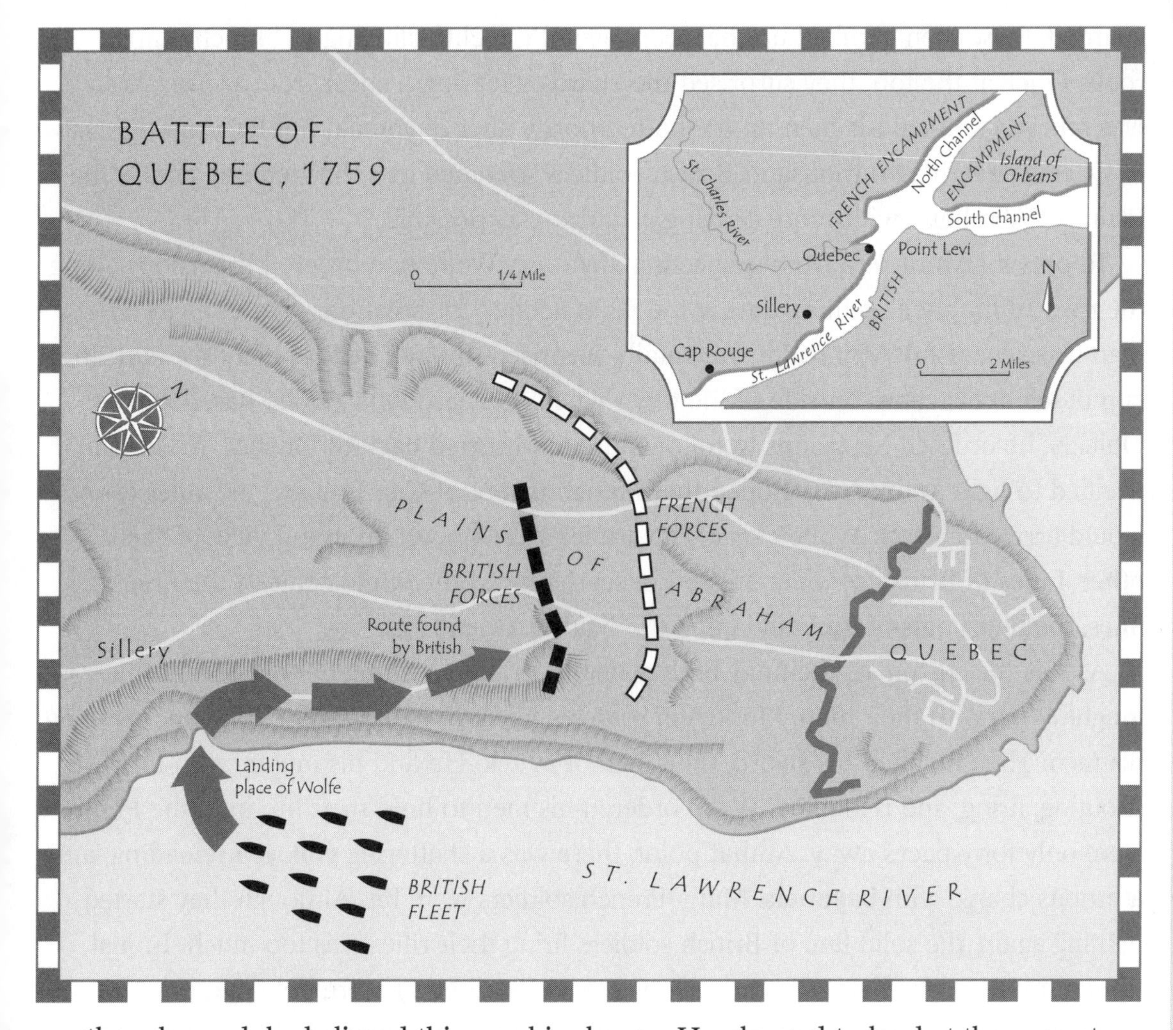

weather changed; he believed this was his chance. He planned to land at the cove at night, using boats from the ships above Quebec. Following the path, he would climb up the cliffs near the town with a large enough force to seize the plateau at the top, which was known as the Plains of Abraham. This piece of land extended to the walls of the town, and there he would fight Montcalm in the open. Wolfe realized that if there was a strong French guard on the height, he would be defeated. In fact, clever Montcalm knew this was a dangerous spot and had kept a regiment there to guard the path. But, again, Governor Vaudreuil had interfered, saying that the English could not fly up the cliffs, and had ordered the soldiers back to the town.

A French deserter told Wolfe that French boats filled with badly needed supplies would try to slip into Quebec on the night of September 12. In fact, the order had been canceled, but the French soldiers standing guard along the shore did not know this. Near midnight on September 12, Wolfe had eighteen hundred men in rowboats near the British warship *Sutherland*. At half past one in the morning, a signal light from the large ship alerted the men that the tide was with them. The boats started moving to shore. When the French sentries called out for identification, a voice answered in good French that they were bringing supplies and warned the sentries to be silent so that the English would not hear.

Wolfe was the first person to leap to shore. Twenty-four specially picked men dashed to the foot of the cliff. Uncertain whether or not the path used by the women would be guarded, these men climbed up the steep face of the cliff, clinging to branches and roots. Once at the top, they surprised the guards. Hearing a cheer from above, Wolfe was relieved and led his men up the path. Shortly after daybreak, not far from the walls of Quebec, nearly two thousand British soldiers stretched in a thin red line across the Plains of Abraham, with more arriving as quickly as possible.

To prevent Montcalm from suspecting anything, Wolfe had ordered the troops along the river to fire their artillery during the night against fortifications farther away. His plan was successful; Montcalm was totally surprised. In fact, he was having a morning cup of tea at his camp outside of the town when he heard what Wolfe had done. Quickly, he ordered his troops to follow him and hurried back to Quebec. Montcalm decided to fight at once. He hoped that French troops at Cap Rouge, four miles away, would arrive to attack Wolfe's rear. The armies were drawn up in full view of each other. Lines of British soldiers dressed in scarlet faced the white coats of the French lines, the blue coats of the militia and the Native Americans.

As was the custom of the time, both generals, in their striking full-dress uniforms, fought along with their men. Montcalm rode his black horse along the lines encouraging his men. Then he lifted his sword, the signal of attack. He and his men moved forward, shouting, firing, and reloading. Wolfe ordered his men to hold their fire until the French were only forty paces away. At that point, there was a shattering **volley**, a reloading, and a furious charge with **bayonets**. Many French soldiers were hit. Although they started fighting again, the solid line of British soldiers firing their rifles was too much. In just fifteen minutes, the fierce battle was over, and the French were defeated.

As the French soldiers retreated, Montcalm rode among them, trying to lead them back into the town. Then a shot pierced his body. He was badly wounded and would have fallen from his horse, but two soldiers held him up and led the horse through the gate of the town. He died at his doctor's house a few hours later. Scared French troops continued to stream toward Quebec, chased by shouting British soldiers. General Wolfe was on foot and leading part of the army when he was shot first in the wrist, then in the lungs. He was carried on a stretcher to the rear of the battlefield. With his last breath, he gave thanks for the British victory.

Quebec surrendered on September 18. A British general received the keys to the city from the French commander. The French flag was taken down and the British flag rose over Quebec. A quick attack by the British might have brought the fall of Montreal, another important French fort, farther down the Saint Lawrence River. But the British generals who were preparing to attack Montreal did not learn that Quebec had fallen until late October. Winter was too near. The British had to wait until 1760 for Montreal to surrender. When a peace agreement was signed in 1763, Britain took over the whole American continent east of the Mississippi River, except the town of New Orleans, which France surrendered to Spain. After controlling a portion of North America for nearly a hundred years, France was left with only two little islands off the south coast of Newfoundland.

accomplished *adj.* good at something; skilled, expert

fortification *n.* something that strengthens and secures, especially military works erected to defend a position or place

foothold *n.* a firm or secure position that provides a base from which to advance

maintain *v.* to carry on; to continue

militia *n.* a group of citizens who receive military training but who are on call only for emergencies

volley *n.* the firing of a number of weapons at the same time

bayonet *n.* a blade attached to a rifle muzzle and used for hand-to-hand fighting

LOOKING BACK AT WHAT YOU HAVE READ

1. What were General James Wolfe's orders?

____

____

2. Why were Wolfe's orders difficult to carry out? List the reasons in order of importance.

____

____

3. Which army, the French or the British, was bigger?

____

____

4. How did Wolfe's keen eye help the British?

____

____

5. How did the jealousy of Governor Vaudreuil hurt the French cause?

____

____

6. How did General Wolfe trick the French?

____

____

7. Just before the English went up the cliff, who was the first to leap to shore?

8. Why was the capture of Quebec so important?

WORKING WITH WORDS

Here are some more **similes**. You may remember that a simile is a phrase or expression introduced by the words *like* or *as*. It compares two things that are not alike.

Example: The noise from the battle was *as loud as thunder.*
This means that the battle was very noisy.

Now explain what these similes mean and use them in sentences.

General Montcalm was *as sly as a fox.*

General Wolfe was *as happy as a lark* when he realized there must be a path from the edge of the river to the level above.

General Wolfe's plan worked *like a charm,* and the French were totally surprised.

Remember **homophones**? They are words that sound alike but are spelled differently and have different meanings.

Example: *horse* and *hoarse*

The young *horse* is very fast.

I cheered so much at the basketball game that my voice became *hoarse*.

In the following passage from the story, there are seven words that are homophones. See if you can find five of them. Write them down; next to each one write its homophone partner.

Montcalm had replied, "I shall do everything to maintain it, or die." He knew that he did not have the troops to attack and defeat Wolfe. His French army was not even half the size of Wolfe's. Although he gathered together ten thousand militia and some Native Americans, they were not experienced soldiers.

CROSSWORD PUZZLE

Use the clues to fill in the puzzle. Then check your answers with each clue. Do they make sense?

Down

1. The ______ report said heavy snow today.

3. He interfered with Montcalm's orders.

4. The name for a large boat

7. ________ of the generals was loved by his troops.

9. This connected the river to the level above.

11. A nickname for the French general (two words)

12. He was drinking tea when he learned the British were outside Quebec.

15. He was the first to leap to shore when the British reached the cove.

16. Both sides used this kind of weapon.

Across

2. The Point from which the British bombarded the French fort

4. A word describing the cliffs by the river

5. This group helped the French fight the British.

6. Wolfe's orders were to capture this place.

8. A ________ from the French army helped the British.

10. The battle between the British and the French took place here. (three words)

13. The first place Wolfe was shot

14. The British used these to go to shore at the cove.

16. Wolfe's rank in the British army

17. The French fort was located at the top of these.

WRITING SKILLS

Pretend you are an officer on General Wolfe's staff. Before General Wolfe dies, he asks you to write a report to his commanding general in London, telling about the battle on the Plains of Abraham and its outcome.

First, write down some key ideas. When you have finished your report, proofread your writing. Does it make sense? Have you included everything you wanted to say? Check it for correct spelling, grammar, capitalization, and punctuation.

Key ideas

Dear General:

Sincerely,

Now pretend you are an assistant to Governor Vaudreuil. Write a letter to the King of France, telling him how and why Quebec fell to the British.

First, write down some key ideas. When you have finished your report, proofread your writing. Does it make sense? Have you included everything you wanted to say? Check it for correct spelling, grammar, capitalization, and punctuation.

Key ideas

To His Majesty, the King of France:

Sincerely,

Louis Armstrong
1901 – 1971

Think about It . . . .

What do you think makes a musician successful?

AS YOU READ Put a ★ beside each important idea in the story. Then write in the margin why each is important. Put a ✓ next to parts of the story that you find interesting. Put a **?** next to parts of the story you do not understand.

Many people remember Louis Armstrong as a fabulous entertainer, the singer with the **distinctive**, gravelly voice. In 1964, his hit vocal recording of "Hello, Dolly!" sold two million copies, moving the Beatles out of first place on the best-seller list. Armstrong was more than a marvelous singer. He was one of the most famous and important performers in the history of jazz. Working as a trumpeter, as a singer, and as the leader of his own musical group, he was a major force in shaping jazz. More than any other musician, Armstrong took jazz out of the African-American quarter of New Orleans where it was born, made it a part of American culture, and introduced it around the world.

Armstrong was born in New Orleans, Louisiana, and lived in great poverty. When Armstrong was growing up, New Orleans was perhaps the most musical city in the United States. Music was everywhere. Near his home, he heard tunes coming from the saloons and dance halls. He listened to the rhythms of the marching bands and funeral processions as well as the music that was played and sung in church. Years later Armstrong wrote, "But man, I sure had a ball there growing up in New Orleans as a kid. We were poor and everything like that, but music was all around you. Music kept you rolling."

When he was a child, Armstrong and his friends formed a quartet, a group of four singers. As they went around the neighborhood, people would ask them to sing. Armstrong recalled, "I used to sing **tenor**, had a real light voice, and played a little slide whistle, like a trombone. . . . After we'd sing, we'd pass the hat–get six bits, maybe even a dollar each for a night."

On New Year's Eve in 1912, Armstrong was out singing with his quartet. People were shooting pistols and setting off firecrackers and roman candles. Armstrong fired a gun, too. Even though it was loaded with blanks, he was arrested and sent to the Colored **Waifs**' Home. There the bandmaster, Peter Davis, asked him if he would like to play in the Home's brass band. When Armstrong said that he did not know how to play an instrument, Davis gave him a bugle to try, and soon Armstrong was playing **reveille** and taps every day. Later, Davis taught him how to play "Home Sweet Home" on the cornet, a kind of trumpet. Before long, Armstrong was the leader of the twenty-piece band.

After spending a year and a half at the Home, Armstrong was released. Since he had to earn money to take care of his mother, he never went back to school but did odd jobs. As soon as he could, he started playing music. When he was seventeen, he got his first job as a musician by playing in a little club.

Joe "King" Oliver, a jazz cornetist and Armstrong's lifelong **idol**, helped him by giving him music lessons and a cornet of his own. In a short time, Armstrong was working with many New Orleans jazz musicians. His golden, clear tone, rhythmic freedom, and amazing ability to **improvise** drew many people to hear him. When he was nineteen, Armstrong began playing in a Mississippi riverboat band that traveled from New Orleans to Saint Louis. Between trips on the boat, a musician in the band taught him to read music.

In 1922, Joe Oliver asked Armstrong to come to Chicago to join his very successful Creole Jazz Band, the best New Orleans group in the North. In 1923, Armstrong, playing the cornet, made his first recording. His experiences with the band allowed him to grow quickly as a musician. He improved his technique and experimented with his instrument. Feeling that the band's style was too controlling, he left Chicago in 1924 to join Fletcher Henderson, a jazz arranger and bandleader, in New York. There, Armstrong played cornet in a big band with top musicians and made a series of unforgettable recordings.

Because he was dissatisfied with the members of the band, Armstrong moved back to Chicago in 1925. This was the beginning of what many critics call his four golden years. He switched to the trumpet and started to do some singing himself. Records were just beginning to be made. He began a series of small band recordings that are among the masterpieces of jazz. Many of these were issued under the names Hot Five and Hot Seven. They show Armstrong's brilliant tone and huge range. In addition, he used a new way of singing. During the Hot Five recording of "Heebie Jeebies" in 1926, Armstrong dropped his sheet music by accident and had to improvise vocally until the recording director could pick up the music for him. He sang without words, using nonsense syllables. This became known as scat singing. In the years to come, many singers would adopt and develop this style of singing.

Armstrong returned to New York in 1928 to start his own band. He began playing popular songs, which he shaped in his own way, along with jazz, blues, and original instrumental numbers. Later, large dance bands followed his example. Armstrong found that he loved performing for an audience. He began talking to them, telling them what the band was going to play and what was happening, instead of going from one number to another without any introduction. In time, his now gravelly voice became as well known as the golden sound of his trumpet. Although still a brilliant trumpeter, he had also become a popular entertainer.

Starting in 1932, Armstrong performed in Europe. People loved his music. The power and the beauty of his musical ideas established his international reputation as the most creative jazz musician alive. Instead of a group of instruments playing the lead in a song as was done in the past, Armstrong began using a single horn. This gave him more time to improvise. The rhythmic freedom he showed in his improvised solos created a style that was to inspire jazzmen and arrangers for many years. The famous jazz trumpeter Miles Davis said, "You can't play anything on a horn that Louis hasn't played."

In 1947, he formed the first of a series of small bands, called the All-Stars, with whom he played for the next twenty years. After World War II, when American soldiers had introduced American jazz around the world, Armstrong's musical tours became enormously popular. On his first trip to Africa in 1956, the one hundred thousand people who had gathered to hear him went wild when he began to blow his trumpet. Besides making thousands of recordings, throughout the years Armstrong appeared in over thirty movies, beginning with *Pennies from Heaven* in 1936.

As he grew older and his health weakened, he played less and sang more. In the summer of 1971, he died. Many people believe that Louis Armstrong is the greatest and most creative jazz musician ever. Armstrong never paid much attention to what people said about him, but he had strong feelings about music. "I don't think you should analyze music. Like the old-timer told me, he say, 'Don't worry about that black cow giving white milk. Just drink the milk.'"

distinctive *adj.* setting one apart by being different; special

tenor *adj.* the highest natural adult male singing voice

waif *n.* homeless child

reveille *n.* a bugle call played at sunrise, announcing the first military formation; a signal to get up in the morning

idol *n.* a person one admires greatly

improvise *v.* to make up and perform something that has not been planned before

LOOKING BACK AT WHAT YOU HAVE READ

1. When he was a boy, what kind of a voice did Armstrong have?

____

____

2. What kind of music did Louis Armstrong hear when he was growing up?

____

____

3. What event led Louis Armstrong to learn how to play a bugle?

____

____

4. What were the qualities of Louis Armstrong's playing that drew people to hear him?

____

____

5. Where did Louis Armstrong play from 1922 to 1924?

____

____

6. What is scat singing?

____

____

7. Why did jazz become popular around the world?

____

____

8. Why do you think Louis Armstrong made music his life's work?

WORKING WITH WORDS

You remember that a **synonym** is a word that has the same or almost the same meaning as another word.

Funny and *amusing* are synonyms.

Armstrong was a brilliant trumpeter. List synonyms for *brilliant*. Try to think of at least four words.

Look at the following phrases from the story. On the lines, write an explanation of what each phrase in bold print means.

Example: **four golden years**

Four golden years means that these were four very creative years for Armstrong.

music **kept you rolling**

people **went wild**

I sure **had a ball.**

Do you remember that a **metaphor** is a phrase that compares two things that are not alike? It is different from a simile because it does not use the words *like* or *as*. Here are two examples.

My mother says that my stomach is *a bottomless pit.*

When the air conditioner stopped working, the room became *a steam bath.*

Below are some metaphors describing Armstrong's life. Explain what each metaphor means. Then, using the metaphor, write your own sentence.

When Armstrong first performed in his neighborhood, was he *a bundle of nerves?*

____

____

Armstrong's legs *turned to rubber* when he was arrested.

____

____

At the Waifs' Home, Peter Davis was *a ray of sunshine* for Armstrong.

____

____

Although Joe Oliver was Armstrong's idol, Armstrong was never *a clinging vine*.

____

____

What do you think Armstrong meant when he said, "Don't worry about that black cow giving white milk. Just drink the milk."

____

____

Write a paragraph about your favorite musician or group. Be sure your paragraph has a title.

First, write down some key ideas. Who are you writing about? Why do you like this musician or group? Are they popular? Why? When you have finished your paragraph, proofread your writing. Does it make sense? Have you included everything you want to say? Check it for correct spelling, grammar, capitalization, and punctuation.

Key ideas

- ____________________
- ____________________
- ____________________
- ____________________

Title:

Louis Armstrong had a very interesting life. What is your life like? Write a four-paragraph composition describing your life today. Be sure to include a title. Talk about what you think is special about your life. You might want to talk about your friends and family and your interests. Put your supporting ideas into separate paragraphs. Make certain that each supporting paragraph has its own topic sentence. You will need one paragraph each for your introduction and conclusion.

First, write an outline for your composition. When you have finished your composition, proofread your writing. Does it make sense? Have you included everything you wanted to say? Check it for correct spelling, grammar, capitalization, and punctuation.

Outline

Introduction

Paragraph 1

Paragraph 2

Conclusion

Title:

Saint PETERSBURG

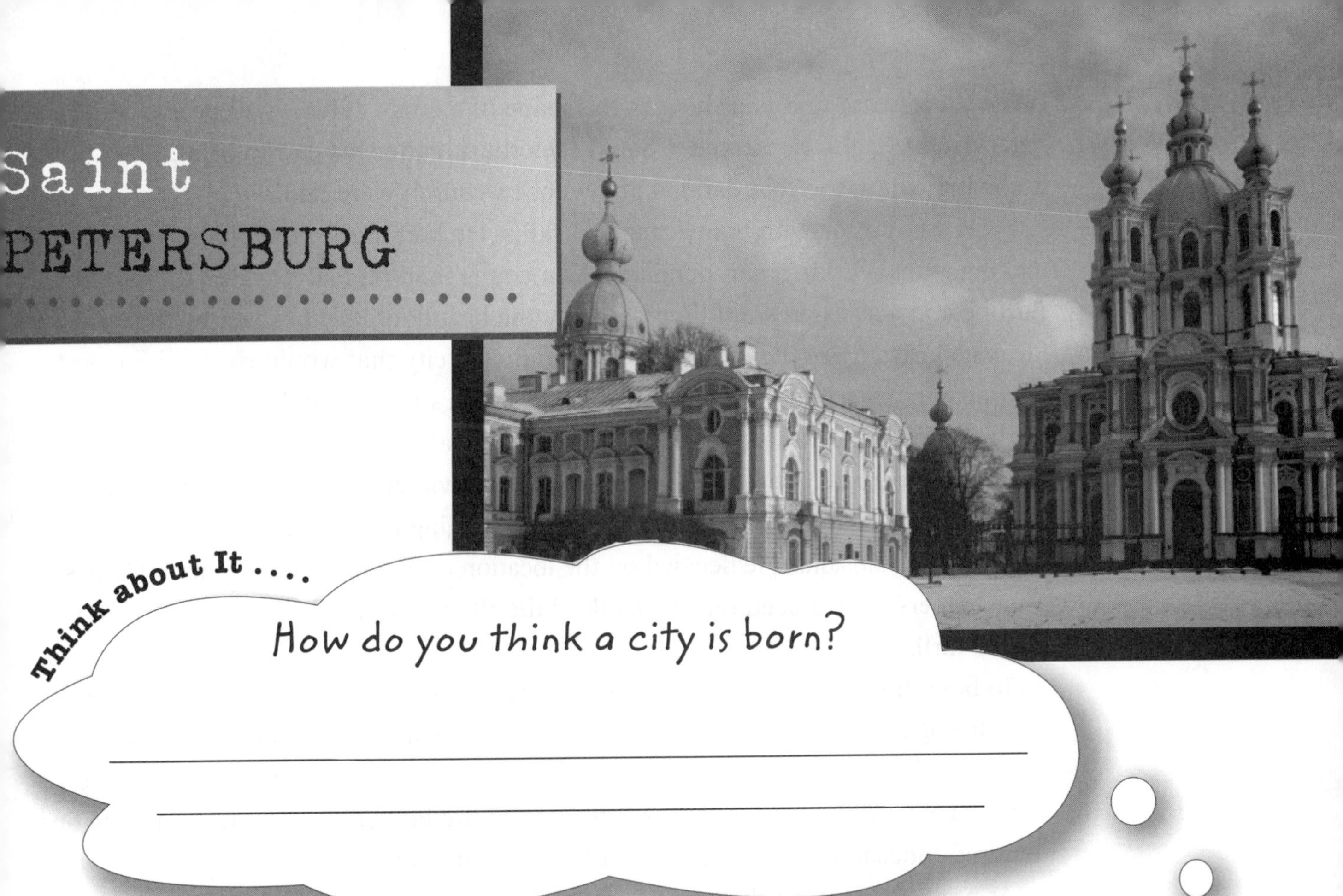

Think about It . . . .

How do you think a city is born?

AS YOU READ Put a ★ beside each important idea in the story. Then write in the margin why each is important. Put a ✓ next to parts of the story that you find interesting. Put a **?** next to parts of the story you do not understand.

OTES

Saint Petersburg is an amazing city. Covering more than forty islands and crisscrossed by at least sixty rivers and canals, it is as flat as a pancake. Like Washington, D.C., Saint Petersburg was built on a swamp, but it is much grander than Washington is. Adding to its beauty is the gold you see everywhere–glimmering on **spires** and glowing on crosses, eagles, statues, and crowns. Among Saint Petersburg's greatest buildings are its famous palaces, painted in blue and white, yellow, green, and rust. Whether these colorful palaces are set off by a blanket of snow in the freezing cold winter or are reflected in the water of the city's canals during a long summer night, they are a magnificent sight.

Saint Petersburg came about because of one man, the powerful leader of Russia in the late 1600s, Czar Peter the Great. In May 1703 when Peter was at war with Sweden, he wanted a fortress from which he could direct future attacks against Finland, which Sweden controlled. In the Gulf of Finland, he found many islands covered with forests. As he explored the area, Peter noticed some land that had been recently abandoned by its Finnish settlers. It was right where the Neva River empties into the Gulf of Finland. There was little to see except reeds and swamps. Peter decided that here he would build his fortress. On May 16, 1703, he cut two pieces of

turf with a sword and laid them in the shape of a cross. "Here shall be a town," Peter declared, and he named it Sankt Pieterburkh after his patron saint. The following month the foundations of a wooden church were laid.

Peter was a czar with many practical skills. He had tried shipbuilding, boot making, metalworking, and dentistry. As a young man he had traveled to Western Europe and was excited and impressed by the beauty of its cities and by the new ideas he heard there. Peter dreamed of building a city that would rival the greatest European cities he had visited. It would be Russia's new capital, replacing Moscow. He hired foreigners to construct this center. An Italian, Domenico Trezzini, produced a very detailed plan for the city. He provided sample designs for inns and shops as well as for different types of houses, ranging from simple rectangular huts to two-story mansions. He decided on the location of the houses and other buildings. Shopkeepers were placed on one bank of the river, and ten thousand craftsmen were placed farther up the river.

To build his city, Peter needed a huge group of workers. **Peasants** and prisoners were brought from every part of Russia. The work was very hard because they had no tools. They had to use their hands or pieces of wood for digging. To move the earth, they used the tails of their shirts. During the first years of building, nearly one hundred thousand workers died from hunger and cold.

As protection against the fires and floods that swept over the islands, Peter wanted the important buildings made of stone. However, since the location was a swamp, rocks were **scarce**. Peter ordered that everybody entering Saint Petersburg had to carry a stone with them; if people came by cart, they had to bring several stones. All of Russia had to help build the city. Forty thousand workmen a year were collected from all parts of Russia. Since the stones had to be brought from far away, building was very costly. In order to pay for this construction, the Russians were forced to pay new and extremely high taxes. Peter prohibited the use of stone as a building material throughout the rest of Russia. This forced all the skilled **masons** to go to Saint Petersburg to find work.

Despite the problems of fires and floods, Peter ordered a thousand families to build homes along the Neva River. Every nobleman who owned thirty families of **serfs** had to put up and pay for a house in the new city. Nobles who owned five hundred serfs or more had to build in stone.

In 1710, Peter erected a Summer Palace near a summer garden, which he had started several years before. Trezzini designed the palace to be similar to other houses in his Saint Petersburg plan. The following year a simple Winter Palace was constructed for Peter. Using tree trunks, workers laid a road over two and a half miles long through the forest. Later, this was named Nevsky Prospect, and today it is the city's main street.

Only nine years after Czar Peter cut the pieces of turf to mark the spot of his new city, he announced that Saint Petersburg, as it came to be spelled, was the new capital of Russia. The Russian court and senate were moved from Moscow, the old capital. The first museums, a library, a theater, an observatory, and an academy of sciences were quickly opened. Near Saint Petersburg, two beautiful palaces, Oranienbaum and Peterhof, were constructed, and a road was laid to Tsarskoe Selo, the future summer home of the czars.

In 1716, Jean-Baptiste Leblond, a Frenchman, became Peter's chief architect. His plans included a system of canals, similar to those used by the Dutch. The canals were supposed to absorb the water from heavy rains and melting snow. Peter's summer garden had existed since 1704. However, after visiting the French palace Versailles, Peter decided in 1717 that he wanted his gardens to be symmetrical or balanced like the gardens at Versailles. One of Leblond's first jobs was to improve the old gardens of the Summer Palace. The architect brought in many different kinds of trees and shrubs. He piped water from the river to the fountains, and he imported unusual birds and animals. Throughout the gardens he placed statues, which he had ordered from England, Holland, and Italy.

When Czar Peter died in 1725, the city was not finished, but he had established the city's plan. There were two fortresses, the Admiralty and Peter and Paul. The Summer Palace and its gardens bounded the city on the east. The Neva's **tributaries** had been redirected, and the Nevsky Prospect had been laid out. Forty thousand people were living in Saint Petersburg, and all of Russia's leading families had built stone houses on this flat marshland.

After Peter's death, two czarinas, Elizabeth and Catherine, added to the city's splendor. In 1754, Czarina Elizabeth I, Peter's daughter, continued building the Winter Palace. Constructed by the Italian architect Bartolomeo Rastrelli, it was built on the river's edge. Outside it had rows of columns and nearly two thousand heavily decorated windows; inside there were one thousand rooms and a hundred staircases. By the time it was finished in 1762, Elizabeth had died, and Catherine the Great ruled.

Peter the Great had started a picture collection, but it was Catherine who made it the world-famous art collection it is today. Other rulers had art that was much finer than Russia's, and Catherine realized that owning great works of art would add to her **prestige**. Only a year after she came to the throne, she bought a collection of 225 paintings. Catherine had wanted a place where she could be alone to relax, so next to the Winter Palace, she arranged to have built a retreat or hermitage and used it for her private apartments. When the paintings arrived in 1764, they were placed there. "Only the mice and I can admire all this," she once said. Catherine would buy many more works of art, and in 1783, she built a large building to house the rest of her art collection. Today, this is known as the Hermitage Museum, which is one of the world's greatest storehouses of art.

During World War I, the name of Saint Petersburg was changed to Petrograd so that it would sound more Russian. In 1917, during the Russian Revolution, the capital was moved back to Moscow. When Lenin, the leader of the Russian Revolution died in 1924, Petrograd's name was changed to Leningrad to honor him. Once Moscow became the capital, the city was quiet and neglected.

At the beginning of World War II, this calm was suddenly broken when, without any warning, Germany invaded Russia. On September 8, 1941, the German army stood at the southern gates of Leningrad, and it would stay there for two and a half terrible years. Germany's plan was to encircle the city and starve the people into surrender. Leningrad only had enough supplies for ten days. Except for what could be brought across Lake Ladoga, the city was completely isolated. There was constant bombing and shelling, but as best they could the people protected their city's art and architecture. Five thousand people died every day, but still the city's life and work went on. By the time the siege ended in January 1944, over eight hundred thousand of the three million people living in the city had died.

During the 1990s the city's name was again changed to Saint Petersburg. Famous for the beauty of its architecture and its wonderful art collections, Saint Petersburg is also remembered for the amazing story of its creation, for its bold rulers, and for its suffering during World War II. It remains one of the world's great cities.

spire *n.* a tall, narrow structure that tapers to a point at the top

turf *n.* the top layer of soil, including grass, small plants, and matted plant roots

peasant *n.* in earlier times, a small farmer or farm laborer, especially in Europe

scarce *adj.* hard to get, rare

mason *n.* a person who builds or works with stone or brick

serf *n.* in earlier times, a farm laborer who was often treated like a slave, and who was completely dependent on the person who owned the land

tributary *n.* smaller river or stream that flows into a larger river or stream

prestige *n.* respect that comes from some great accomplishment

LOOKING BACK AT WHAT YOU HAVE READ

On the lines under each of the three boxes, write important details from the story that give information about these topics.

Saint Petersburg

Peter the Great	Catherine the Great	World War II

WORKING WITH WORDS

Peter the Great was a complex person. Try to think of at least six **adjectives** that describe what he was like.

______________ ______________ ______________

______________ ______________ ______________

______________ ______________ ______________

In an **analogy**, you are trying to figure out the connection between two pairs of words.

Example: Sweden is to country as Moscow is to ______________.

First, you must understand the connection between the words in the first pair, Sweden/country. Make a picture in your mind of these words. Think how they are related. Then make a sentence describing what you see.

Sweden *is* a country.

Now use the word you have pictured to make the same connection between the second pair of words.

Moscow *is* a city.

The analogy, then, is Sweden is to country as Moscow is to city.

In the following analogies, decide what the connection is between the first pair of words. Make a picture of these words in your mind. Think how they are related. Next, write a word in the blank that will show the same connection between the second pair of words.

Peter the Great is to czar as Abraham Lincoln is to ______________.

Mason is to stone as carpenter is to ______________.

Museum is to art as zoo is to ______________.

Czar is to czarina as prince is to ______________.

Leblond is to architect as Wayne Gretzky is to ______________.

Russia is to Saint Petersburg as France is to ______________.

Neva is to river as Nevsky Prospect is to ______________ .

Look at the following words and phrases from the story. On the lines, write a sentence using each of the words or phrases in bold print.

Example: were **imported**

Many products are imported from China.

is **as flat as a pancake**

____

____

glimmering on spires

____

____

set off by a **blanket of snow**

____

____

many **practical skills**

____

____

built a **retreat**

____

____

WRITING SKILLS

For Catherine the Great, the Hermitage was a wonderful place. Do you have such a place? If you do not, imagine what your special place would be like. Make a picture in your mind. Then, in one paragraph describe this place.

First, write down some key ideas. When you have finished your paragraph, proofread your writing. Does it make sense? Have you included everything you wanted to say? Check it for correct spelling, grammar, capitalization, and punctuation.

Key ideas

MY SPECIAL PLACE

An expanded paragraph is one in which you use several supporting ideas to develop your main idea. To make your meaning clear, you should use transition words. These words give the signal that you have finished discussing one supporting idea and are ready to move to the next. Remember that these words are always followed by a comma. Here are some common transition words.

first second next last finally

If you could construct your own dream city, what would it be like? Write an expanded paragraph about your dream city. Where would it be—on the banks of a river or a lake, in a valley, on a hill? What would the buildings be like? What would people do for amusement in your city? Would there be any tourist attractions? Try to use at least three of the transition words above. Be sure that your paragraph has a topic sentence, which gives the main idea of the paragraph, and a concluding sentence, which lets the reader know that you have finished your discussion.

First, write down some key ideas. When you have finished your paragraph, proofread your writing. Does it make sense? Have you included everything you wanted to say? Check it for correct spelling, grammar, capitalization, and punctuation.

Key ideas

MY DREAM CITY

Ferdinand Magellan 1480?–1521

Think about It . . . .

What is a hardship you have experienced?

AS YOU READ Put a ★ beside each important idea in the story. Then write in the margin why each is important. Put a ✓ next to parts of the story that you find interesting. Put a **?** next to parts of the story you do not understand.

OTES

Not only did Ferdinand Magellan's 1519 voyage around the world provide the first proof that the earth is round, but it also showed that two-thirds of the earth's surface is water. Sadly, even though it was Magellan's planning and brave leadership that made the entire voyage possible, he did not live to complete it.

Magellan was the younger son of a noble Portuguese family. When he was seven, he started his religious instruction and began learning the basics of Latin and math. His father arranged for him and his brother to work as **pages** for Queen Leonora at her court in Lisbon, Portugal. Magellan attended a school for pages. There he studied music, dancing, horsemanship, hunting with a hawk and a hound, **jousting**, mapmaking, and the basics of astronomy and navigation.

While working in the queen's household, he learned all the latest news about the voyages of great explorers. He may even have been present when Christopher Columbus visited the Portuguese court after returning from his first voyage in 1493. Magellan dreamed of going to sea with a career in the navy, but in 1495 these hopes were cruelly destroyed when Queen Leonora's husband, King John, was poisoned. Duke Manuel, the queen's brother, became king of Portugal. Even though Magellan had studied very hard from the time he became a student at the page school in 1492,

Duke Manuel had taken a strong dislike to him. When Manuel became king, he prevented Magellan from making a career in the navy.

Magellan gained some experience working with ships, however. At sixteen, he became a clerk in a new marine department in the palace. There he helped equip Vasco da Gama's new fleet that set out for India in 1497. When da Gama returned twenty-six months later, not only had he found the way to India by sailing east around Africa, but he also brought back a cargo of valuable spices. There was a great need for spices in Europe. They were used as **preservatives**. In addition, their seasoning covered up the unpleasant flavor of meat when it was spoiled, and they improved the tasteless food. Spices were so valuable that they were often used instead of money.

In 1500, when a second Portuguese **expedition** was sent to India, Magellan again was disappointed not to be chosen to work on any of the thirteen ships making the voyage. Instead, he had to work hard equipping the ships for the lucky ones who were going. Finally, in 1505, Magellan got a chance to go to sea, not as an explorer, but as a soldier. He was sent on a military expedition to India by way of Africa.

Da Gama had brought back spices from India, but in 1511 the Portuguese sailed directly to the place where the spice plants grew. This was the Spice Islands, now known as the Moluccas, between present-day Indonesia and New Guinea. The Portuguese explorers claimed the islands for Portugal. One of Magellan's friends, Francisco Serrao, was on this voyage and wrote to Magellan, "I have found here a new world richer and greater than that of Vasco da Gama." Serrao liked the islands so much that he decided to stay and suggested that Magellan join him. But Magellan wanted to sail as an explorer.

Magellan became convinced that he could find a shorter way to the Spice Islands. All the earlier explorers had sailed east around Africa to go to India. After studying the best maps, he realized there might be a shorter route by going around the southern tip of the newly discovered Americas. Magellan desperately wanted King Manuel's support, but when he finally met him and asked for aid, the king refused. He shouted **spitefully** that he did not care what Magellan did or where he went. He even denied Magellan the right to kiss his hand in farewell. At that time, this was a great insult.

Magellan did not give up his idea of an expedition to the Spice Islands by sailing west rather than east. Working with a friend, he determined that the Spice Islands lay in territory that belonged by treaty to Spain. So Magellan decided to go to Spain to ask King Charles for support. In 1517, Magellan went to Seville, Spain, and met one of his old friends. Magellan fell in love with his friend's daughter. When the couple married, Magellan became a Spanish citizen and he gained an important father-in-law who knew how to attract King Charles's attention.

The following year, Magellan met King Charles and convinced the young king that he had secret knowledge of a **strait**. He was confident that he could sail through the strait and around the world to claim the Spice Islands for Spain. When the king questioned him as to what he would do if he could not find the strait, Magellan calmly answered that he would just turn around and travel to the Spice Islands the old way, around the

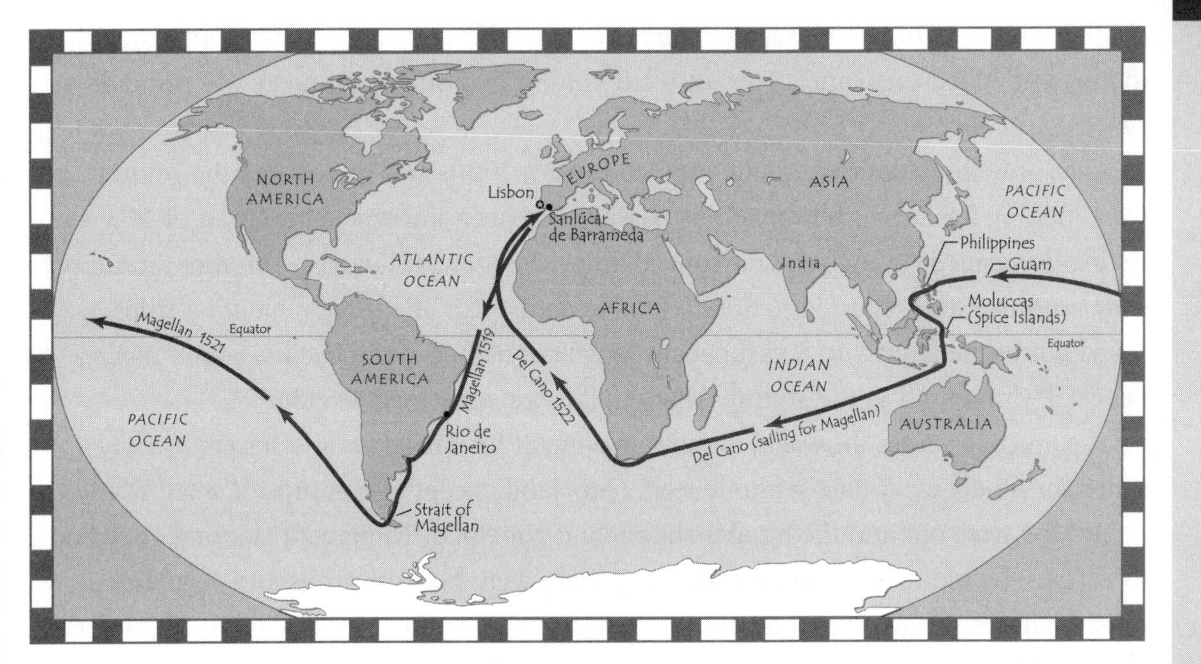

tip of Africa. King Charles agreed to back Magellan's expedition and promised him a fifth of the profits as well as a salary. Although some of the king's advisors believed in supporting the voyage, they were not impressed with Magellan and did not trust him. How could he know of a secret passage when he had never sailed there? They felt that the king had promised Magellan too large a portion of the profits. They started plotting against him even before the trip began.

It took more than a year to prepare for the expedition, and problems developed at once. The Spaniards' suspicions about Magellan grew when he hired many Portuguese sailors. The king forced him to replace most of the Portuguese with Spanish crewmen. When the ships were ready to sail, there was a church service during which the four captains of the ships took an oath that they would obey Magellan's orders. They swore "to follow the course lorded by him and to obey him in everything." Yet three of these men were already secretly determined to rebel against Magellan and to murder him the first chance they had.

On September 20, 1519, Magellan's fleet of five little ships, the *Concepcion, San Antonio, Santiago, Trinidad,* and *Victoria*, set sail from Sanlucar de Barrameda in southern Spain. Aboard were 241 men. From the start, the crewmen were discontented, especially the Spaniards. About a month after the voyage began, Juan de Cartagena, one of the captains determined to oppose Magellan, declared he would no longer obey him. Holding the captain firmly by the front of his shirt, Magellan shouted, "Rebel, this is **mutiny**! In the name of the king you are my prisoner!" When the other two captains did not join him, de Cartagena was furious and revealed their plan to stab Magellan. His followers were also arrested.

Magellan crossed the Atlantic Ocean to the coast of South America where Rio de Janeiro now stands. Then he sailed south looking for a strait to the ocean on the other side. Unable to find a passage before winter, Magellan had his fleet wait for spring in what is now southern Argentina. During the winter, a storm destroyed the *Santiago*, and another mutiny broke out. Magellan and the men who were loyal to him put down the mutiny and killed the leader. They also left behind two other mutineers when the fleet sailed again.

After only three days of sailing, on October 21, 1520, they discovered the route they were looking for. From that time, this passage has been known as the Strait of Magellan. As the fleet sailed through the narrow channel, the crew of the *San Antonio*, the supply ship, mutinied and returned to Spain. On November 28, the three remaining ships sailed out of the strait into a vast ocean. Magellan named it the Pacific, which means peaceful. Compared to the stormy Atlantic, this water seemed so calm.

The journey across the Pacific was very difficult for Magellan and his crew. They sailed for ninety-eight days without seeing any land except two groups of small islands. Their food gave out and their water supply had gone bad. To prevent starving, they had to eat rats, ox hides, and sawdust. Because there were no fresh fruits and vegetables, most of the crew had scurvy, a painful disease caused by the lack of vitamin C. Nineteen men died before they reached Guam on March 6, 1521.

Conflicts with the people of Guam and the nearby island of Rota prevented Magellan from fully resupplying his ships. But the crew seized enough food and water to continue to the Philippine Islands. Magellan and his crew stayed there for several weeks. They became friendly with the islanders. Magellan was very pleased when many islanders decided to **convert** to Christianity.

Unfortunately, when two Filipino groups on one of the islands started a fight, Magellan joined in the battle and was killed on April 27, 1521. A shipmate of Magellan described his brave death in these words, "When they wounded him, he turned back many times to see whether we were all in the boats. . . . Thus the natives killed our mirror, our light, our comfort, and our true guide. . . . Had it not been for that unfortunate Captain, not a single one of us would have been saved, for while he was fighting, the others retired to the boats, which were already pulling off."

With only about 110 men remaining, the captains had to leave one ship behind. They sailed the other two southward to the Spice Islands and loaded them with spices. To make sure one of the ships got back to Spain, the captains decided that they each should take a different route. The *Trinidad* sailed eastward, returning through the Strait of Magellan. But when more than half of the crew died, the rest were forced to sail back to the Spice Islands. There the Portuguese residents made them prisoners. The *Victoria* continued sailing westward to Spain; many on this ship also died. On September 6, 1522, nearly three years after all five ships had set out on their journey, just one, the *Victoria*, returned to Spain. Only the commander and seventeen others survived.

One of the crew on the *Victoria* was an Italian named Antonio Pigafetta. Throughout the voyage he kept a journal, which is the chief source of information about the expedition. He praised Magellan for his courage and navigational skill, but nearly everyone else at the time gave Juan Sebastian del Cano, the commander of the *Victoria*, the credit for the voyage. Even though Magellan was not able to find a short route to the Spice Islands, his voyage added greatly to our knowledge about the earth. With the discovery of the Strait of Magellan, other European expeditions would go on to explore the vast Pacific.

page *n.* long ago, a boy trained to serve an important person

joust *n.* a formal contest or combat between two knights on horseback

preservative *n.* a substance that keeps something from spoiling or decaying

expedition *n.* a long journey or voyage made for a specific purpose such as exploration

spitefully *adv.* showing a feeling of ill will toward another

strait *n.* a narrow waterway connecting two large bodies of water

mutiny *n.* an open rebellion by a group against its leaders; especially, rebellion of soldiers or sailors against their officers

convert *v.* to change from one belief or religion to another

LOOKING BACK AT WHAT YOU HAVE READ

Ferdinand Magellan led an exciting life. On the time line below write down the important events of his life. Be sure to include dates when possible. Draw pictures, if you wish, of the events you marked down.

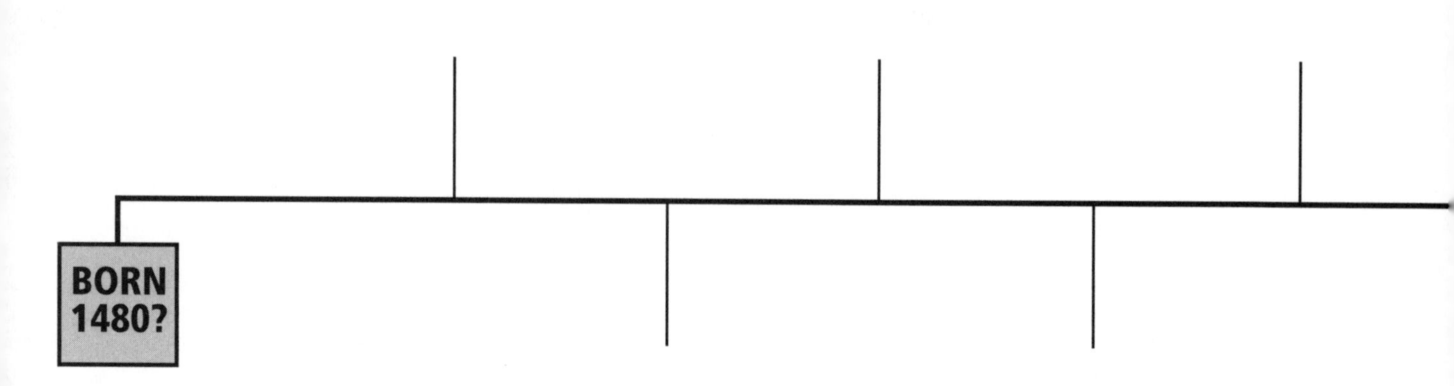

DIED
1521

WORKING WITH WORDS

Think of **adjectives** that describe the following people. You may want to go back to the story to see what they were like. Try to think of three adjectives that describe each of the following people.

Ferdinand Magellan	**King Charles**
______________	______________
______________	______________
______________	______________
______________	______________

King Manuel	**Juan de Cartagena**
______________	______________
______________	______________
______________	______________
______________	______________

Do you remember **idioms**? An idiom is a group of words that have a special meaning. If you do not know the special meaning, you will not understand what a person is saying. It may even sound ridiculous. For example, "To pay through the nose." This means that you pay much too much for something.

Read the explanations of the following idioms. Then write a sentence using the idiom.

The idiom "green with envy" means to be very jealous.

When Magellan was not chosen to work on any of the thirteen ships going to India, he was green with envy.

____

____

The idiom "the fly in the ointment" means one small part that spoils the whole thing.

For Magellan, King Manuel was the fly in the ointment.

____

____

The idiom "feather in your cap" means an accomplishment to be very proud of.

When King Charles of Spain agreed to back Magellan, it was a feather in Magellan's cap.

____

____

De Cartagena was furious when the other two captains would not join him in opposing Magellan. Think of words that mean the same or nearly the same as *furious*. Make a list. Then make a word line by arranging them in a sequence to show degrees of feeling furious.

Example: attractive

List: pleasing nice beautiful fascinating fair agreeable attractive

Word Line: fair agreeable nice attractive pleasing fascinating beautiful

furious

List: ____

Word line: ____

WRITING SKILLS

Your class is studying the great explorers of the world and you have been assigned Ferdinand Magellan. Every student must give a speech about his or her explorer. In your speech you will talk about what the explorer accomplished and give the highlights of his life. Because you might get nervous, you decide to write out your speech and memorize it.

First, write down some key ideas. When you have finished your speech, proofread your writing. Does it make sense? Have you included everything you wanted to say? Check it for correct spelling, grammar, capitalization, and punctuation.

Key ideas

- ______________________
- ______________________
- ______________________
- ______________________

Ferdinand Magellan, a Great Explorer

____

____

____

____

____

____

____

____

____

____

____

____

____

____

From history books, we know that the page school Magellan attended was outstanding. Imagine that you are asked to create your own outstanding school. Write a four-paragraph composition about the school you will develop. Describe your plan for the school. How will your school be special? What are the facilities and teachers like? What will the students study? What will the schedule be? Choose two points you wish to discuss in your composition.

Be sure to include a title. Put your supporting ideas into separate paragraphs. Make certain each supporting paragraph has its own topic sentence. You will need one paragraph each for your introduction and conclusion.

First, write an outline for your composition. When you have finished your composition, proofread your writing. Does it make sense? Have you included everything you wanted to say? Check it for correct spelling, grammar,
capitalization, and punctuation.

Outline

Introduction

Paragraph 1

Paragraph 2

Conclusion

Title:

Writing the UNIVERSAL DECLARATION OF HUMAN RIGHTS

Think about It . . . .

How can people make sure that everyone is treated fairly?

____

____

AS YOU READ Put a ★ beside each important idea in the story. Then write in the margin why each is important. Put a ✓ next to parts of the story that you find interesting. Put a **?** next to parts of the story you do not understand.

NOTES

In April 1945, World War II was coming to an end. **Delegates** from fifty countries arrived in San Francisco for the first meeting of the founding conference of the United Nations. Many of the people at the gathering had been inspired by President Franklin Roosevelt's speech in 1941 about four freedoms. In this speech, Roosevelt said that future peace and safety were linked to respect for four freedoms: freedom of speech and expression, freedom to worship God in one's own way, freedom from want, and freedom from fear. The smaller countries decided that they wanted to set up an international standard against which every nation's behavior could be measured.

In 1946, the United Nations (UN) established the Human Rights Commission. Its job was to write the first **Universal** Declaration of Human Rights, listing the rights of all people. During the war millions of innocent people had been killed. Many smaller countries, as well as religious and **humanitarian** groups, wanted to make sure that so many people would never be so badly treated again.

In January 1947, the Human Rights Commission held its first meeting at the UN's temporary headquarters in an old factory building in Lake Success, New York. There were delegates from eighteen member countries: China, France, Great Britain, the Soviet Union, and the United States, and thirteen other countries. Eleanor Roosevelt, the **widow** of President Franklin Roosevelt, was the delegate to the Commission from the United States. No one was surprised when she was **unanimously** elected chairman of the Commission. For much of her life she had been a forceful champion of humanitarian causes. Roosevelt was considered by many to be "the most important person in the United Nations human rights program" and was a powerful reminder of her husband, who had been a strong, early supporter of the UN.

For any declaration to be accepted, the laws of the UN required that two-thirds of the nations that were members would have to agree with it. The members of the Commission knew that if they wanted to write a declaration that would be meaningful worldwide, they would have to overcome obstacles. Not only were there differences in language, culture, and politics among the delegates, but also some of them did not get along with each other. When relations between the Soviet Union and the United States worsened and new world problems developed, the committee members realized they would have to work quickly.

John Humphrey, a Canadian lawyer and head of the UN Secretariat, had prepared a rough draft, or first version, of what should be included in the declaration. Before Humphrey wrote his draft, he and his UN staff carefully studied human rights material sent to the UN by different government and private groups from all over the world. Then on June 9, 1947, eight of the committee members, who represented nations that often had very different opinions on how to deal with the world's problems, met at the UN's headquarters at Lake Success. Their job was to write the draft of the Universal Declaration of Human Rights. Quickly deciding that the group was still too large, they agreed that four members of the group–Rene Cassin, the French delegate, Charles Malik, the delegate from Lebanon, Geoffrey Wilson, the British delegate, and Eleanor Roosevelt–should prepare the draft. These four people agreed that the draft would have more unity if one person wrote it. Cassin, who was considered a legal genius, was asked to do this using Humphrey's rough draft. Cassin included most of the content of Humphrey's paper but gave it greater unity. He also decided to add a preamble, or introduction, where he explained the "why" of the declaration.

In December 1947, the full Human Rights Commission met in Geneva, Switzerland, to look over and make any necessary changes to Cassin's document. Roosevelt was eager to finish the work before Christmas and laid out a work schedule that included night sessions. She wanted the committee to shorten the draft and to put it into language "which could be readily understood by the ordinary man or woman." During long meetings the delegates discussed each part of the paper, sometimes working late into the night. Roosevelt wrote to her daughter, "The work here has been a constant drive & for that reason I will be glad when it is over." By December 12, the Commission had a revised draft for discussion.

At this point, a number of countries began objecting to some of the Commission's ideas about how the Declaration would be used. The main question was what would happen if a nation did not respect the Declaration. Some countries feared that other countries might be able to come into their country and enforce the Declaration against their wishes.

When the drafting committee met again in May 1948 in New York, Roosevelt set out a strict schedule so that the work of having a final document to present to the full Human Rights Commission could be finished in just nine days. Even though there was a war going on in the Middle East and the members of the committee supported different sides of the **conflict**, work on the Declaration continued. When the committee had problems and the delegate from the Soviet Union suggested that they tear up what they had written and start fresh, Roosevelt gently asked him to help improve the draft. She reminded him that the world is made up of many states with many forms of government and that they all had to work together.

To help the delegates to get to know each other and to give them the opportunity to talk freely and "off the record," Roosevelt had dinners and teas at her home in New York City. On June 18, the Human Rights Commission approved the Declaration. Twelve voted in favor and none voted against it. Following their governments' orders, the Soviet Union, Byelorussia, the Ukraine, and Yugoslavia did not vote. The next step was to send this draft Declaration to all UN member states for their advice and comments.

In September 1948, the UN General Assembly held its fall meeting in Paris. The committee members were eager to pass the document. The United States and the Soviet Union were in conflict in Germany and Korea. The state of Israel had just been formed and the Arab countries were at war with Israel. For these reasons, the leaders of the Human Rights Commission knew that if the Declaration did not pass now, it might never pass. But before the General Assembly could vote on the Declaration, it had to be approved by a committee at the UN. Because she was chairman of the Human Rights Commission, Roosevelt presented the draft to this committee. She explained that it was a statement of principles, which set up "a common standard of achievement for all peoples and all nations."

The committee then began examining the document. There were long debates about each point in the Declaration. After a month only three of the thirty articles in the Declaration were approved. Charles Malik, who was chairman of the committee, announced that it would begin holding night sessions. Lindstrom, the Swedish delegate, suggested a three-minute limit on any speeches about the articles and bought a stopwatch. The committee started working faster. On December 7, at three in the morning, the committee approved the draft and said it could be proposed to the General Assembly.

On December 9, 1948, Malik introduced the Universal Declaration of Human Rights to the General Assembly. Reminding the delegates that thousands of minds had helped in its formation, he explained that it was the first time that the principles of human rights and basic freedoms had been stated in exact detail. Roosevelt spoke next and praised the Declaration as an important step in the unfinished job of lifting human beings everywhere "to a higher standard of life and to a greater enjoyment of freedom." At four minutes before midnight on December 10, the president of the General Assembly called the roll. Thirty-four delegates gave speeches supporting the document. The final vote showed forty-eight members in favor, eight members who did not vote, and none who voted against it. The president of the General Assembly closed the session by praising Roosevelt. Then the whole General Assembly rose to applaud her and cheer.

With the passage of the Universal Declaration of Human Rights, a new age in the history of human rights began. Countries that were created after World War II looked carefully at the Declaration and patterned the rights in their constitutions on the rights listed there. The principles listed in the Declaration helped human rights organizations to spotlight cruel treatment and to organize **grassroots** support for change. By saying that all the rights listed in the Declaration belong to everyone, everywhere, the Declaration asserted that all people had certain rights as human beings that no government could take away.

delegate *n.* a person or group of persons chosen to speak and act for another or others; a representative

universal *adj.* relating to or affecting the whole world; worldwide

humanitarian *adj.* concerned with or promoting the general well-being of humanity

widow *n.* a woman whose husband has died

unanimously *adv.* based on or showing complete agreement

conflict *n.* a state of disagreement, as between persons, ideas, or interests

grassroots *adj.* coming from the basic or local level of a community rather than from a higher level of power and control

LOOKING BACK AT WHAT YOU HAVE READ

1. What events inspired people to get together and write a Universal Declaration of Human Rights?

___

___

2. How many countries were represented at the first Human Rights Commission meeting?

___

___

3. Who prepared the first rough draft of the Declaration of Human Rights?

___

___

4. When people in a new country write their constitution, why do they look carefully at the Universal Declaration of Human Rights?

___

___

5. In which country or countries do you think people would be happier if human rights were more closely enforced? Explain your answer.

___

___

6. In order to be a successful chairman of the Human Rights Commission, what qualities do you think Eleanor Roosevelt needed to have?

____

____

7. As the revised draft of the Declaration was being discussed, why did some countries object to how it would be used?

____

____

8. In order for the work on the Declaration to proceed as quickly and as smoothly as possible, what did some members of the commission have to do?

____

____

WORKING WITH WORDS

Word Puzzle

Using the letters in the word DECLARATION, see how many small words you can make. You may use a letter twice in your word if it appears twice in this word.

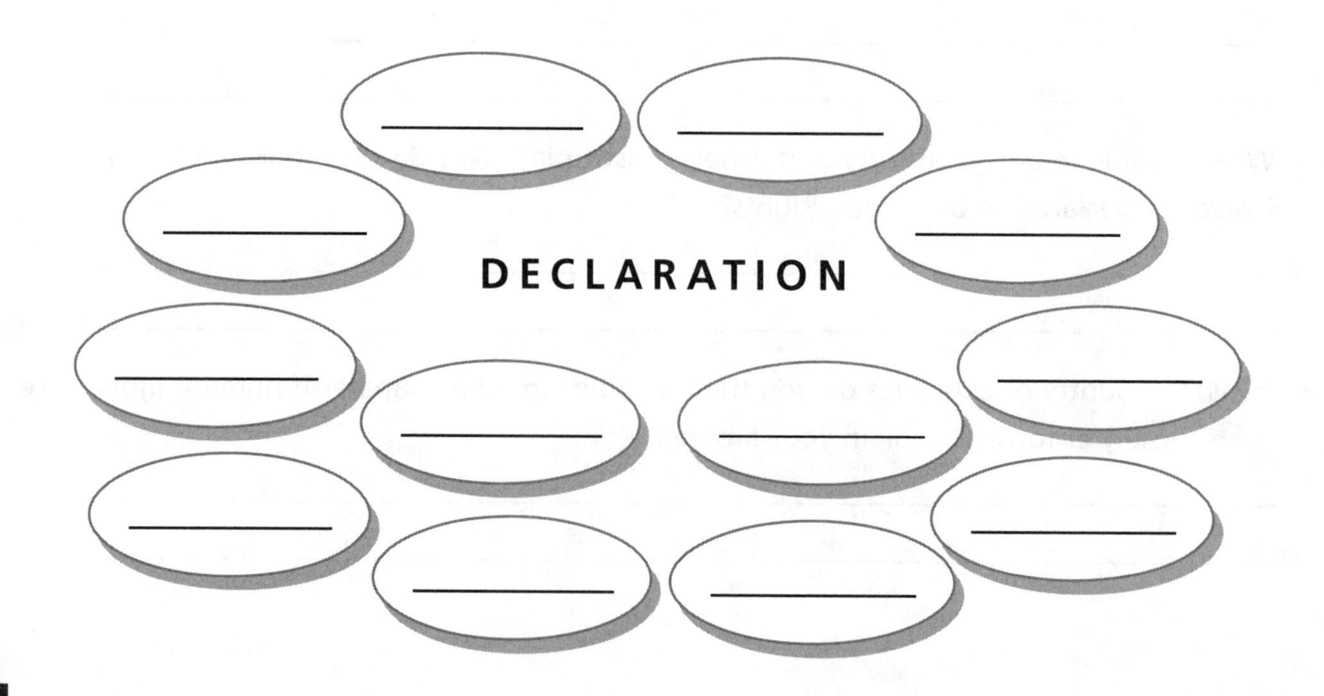

Look at the following phrases from the story. On the lines, write a sentence using each of the phrases that are in bold print.

Example:

a legal genius

You have to be a legal genius to solve this problem.

wanted to set up an **international standard**

____

____

the work here has been a **constant drive**

____

____

to talk freely and **off the record**

____

____

tear up what they had written and **start fresh**

____

____

to organize **grassroots support**

____

____

Do you remember that a **simile** is a phrase or expression introduced by the words *like* or *as*? It compares two things that are not alike.

Example: The sickly child was *as thin as a rail.*

Explain what the simile above means. Try to use it in a sentence.

Now explain what the following similes mean and use them in sentences.

Some of the delegates were *as stubborn as mules.*

Sometimes Roosevelt thought the delegates were *as slow as molasses.*

When the Declaration was passed, Eleanor Roosevelt's eyes sparkled *like diamonds.*

WRITING SKILLS

From 1935 to 1962, Eleanor Roosevelt wrote a newspaper column called *My Day* that appeared six days a week. Pretend you are Eleanor Roosevelt. It is December 11, 1948, the day after the Declaration was passed, and you have to write your column. What will you say? Will you talk about what just happened at the General Assembly and how you feel about the Declaration? Perhaps you will write about something else.

Use as many paragraphs as you need. Be sure that your article has a title and that each paragraph has a topic sentence, which gives the main idea.

First, write down some key ideas. When you have finished your article, proofread your writing. Does it make sense? Have you included everything you wanted to say? Check it for correct spelling, grammar, capitalization, and punctuation.

Key ideas

Title:

You probably know that all students attending school in the United States have certain rights. Imagine that this is not so. You and a group of your fellow students want to propose a bill of rights for students to your local school board. First, you must write down the rights you think students should have. Then list them in order of importance; put the most important rights first.

Now write a letter to the school board in which you discuss why students need a bill of rights and what your bill of rights would include. When you have finished your letter, proofread your writing. Does it make sense? Have you included everything you wanted to say? Check it for correct spelling, grammar, capitalization, and punctuation.

Key ideas

Dear Members of the School Board:

Sincerely,

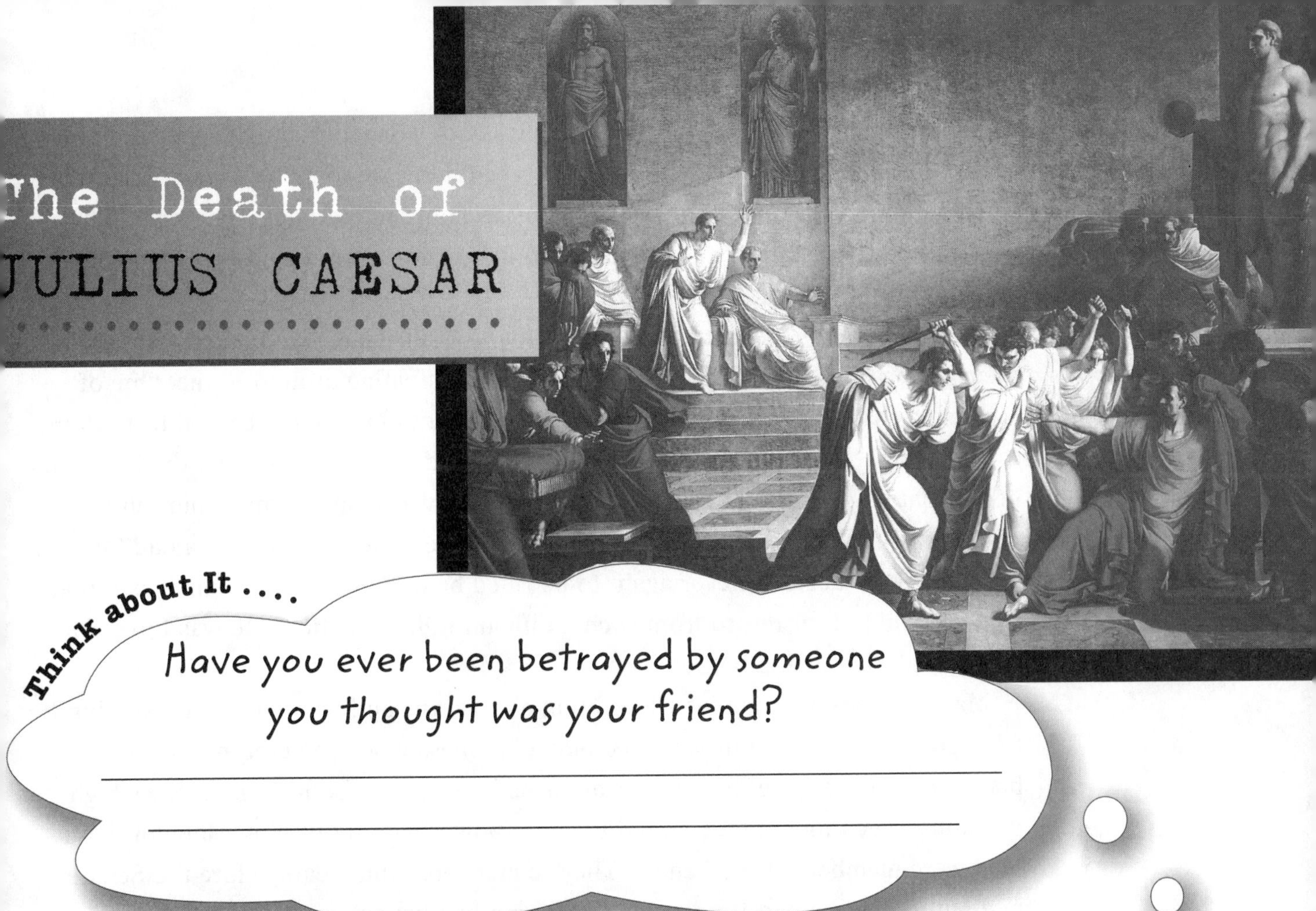

The Death of Julius Caesar

Think about It ....

Have you ever been betrayed by someone you thought was your friend?

AS YOU READ Put a ★ beside each important idea in the story. Then write in the margin why each is important. Put a ✓ next to parts of the story that you find interesting. Put a **?** next to parts of the story you do not understand.

OTES

Waking on the morning of the fifteenth, Julius Caesar said that he did not feel well. Upset by the strange events of the night and by his wife's begging him to stay safely at home, he sent for Mark Antony, a trusted friend, to tell him that he wanted to postpone his visit to the Senate. His doctors had advised him to rest, and the fortune-tellers reported that the animal sacrifices showed that the day was not favorable. At that time, it was the custom for a Roman priest to try to tell the future by looking at the insides of a sacrificed animal. The night before, as Caesar was lying in bed, there had been a sudden blast of wind, and his armor had fallen from the wall. His wife, Calpurnia, had moaned in her sleep. When Caesar woke her, Calpurnia said that she had dreamed he was murdered.

This is a story about a murder that would change the ancient world. The day was March 15, 44 B.C. Julius Caesar, the great military genius, whom the Roman people had made **dictator**, had plans to march very soon with his armies against the Parthians. They were a powerful people living in the area that is now Iran. If he conquered them, Roman rule would reach to the Persian Gulf and even to India. Knowing that he would be away with the army for many years, Caesar planned to talk to the Senate, the ruling body of the Roman Empire, on March 15.

Just days before, a famous fortune-teller had come to Caesar warning him to be careful on the **Ides** of March. But Caesar was not worried, saying that he did not believe in **omens**. On the night of the fourteenth, he ate dinner with a few friends. Knowing that soon they would be going off to fight and perhaps to be killed, the men started to talk about how they would like to die. Caesar said that he wanted a quick, unexpected death.

Rome was in a state of uncertainty. Many Romans feared and hated Caesar, and their feelings were expressed in the many rumors floating around Rome. One of these said that after conquering Parthia, Caesar would move the capital from Rome to Alexandria. Caesar may not really have planned this move, but just the idea made people hate him. Another rumor was that Caesar was going to make himself king with the help of some of the senators. Years before, after living under a bad king, the Roman people decided never again to be ruled by one. Still other rumors said that Caesar would never return from such a difficult military action. He was too old and weak to survive such a battle.

Many of Caesar's enemies viewed him as a **tyrant** and wanted to remove him from power. A group of important Roman families, called the Optimates, would benefit if he were gone. Although Caesar had given men from these families high positions, they thought they would be more powerful without him. Many of these men were members of the Senate. They remembered that years before the Senate had put to death a bad Roman king. Killing a bad king was considered a brave act. As senators, these men had given their oath to protect Caesar. But now they felt their promise of loyalty no longer bound them since Caesar had become a tyrant.

Who were the leaders of this plot? All were members of the Senate and many had been friends of Caesar's. The main leader was Gaius Cassius, a respected general. Cassius was against one man having complete power, and he was also angry because Caesar had not given him a job that he thought he deserved. Caesar had not trusted him for some time and had even said, "Cassius looks so pale. What can he be up to?"

Cassius had convinced his brother-in-law, Marcus Brutus, to join him in planning Caesar's murder. Brutus was young and smart, and Caesar treated him like a son. Decimus Brutus, another **traitor**, had been a favorite of Caesar's for many years and was one of his best generals. About sixty senators were involved in the plot.

The traitors decided that the senate meeting on March 15 would be the perfect time to commit the murder because they were sure that Caesar would be present. This was the moment when the traitors expected him to ask the Senate to confirm him as king. Not only would it be the ideal time, but it would also be the ideal place. Killing Caesar in the Senate would make all of the senators part of the murder.

On the morning of March 15, the traitors waited for Caesar to appear in the Senate. Time passed and he did not arrive. Worried that Caesar had learned of their plan and was sending his soldiers to get them, they sent Decimus Brutus to Caesar's home to convince him to attend the senate meeting.

Persuaded by Brutus, Caesar started traveling through the crowded streets of

Rome. As he rode, Artemidorus, who once had worked as Caesar's secretary, ran after him excitedly waving a message. Years before, Artemidorus had also tutored Marcus Brutus. At the senate building, Caesar brushed aside some men asking for favors, telling them to speak to his officers. He noticed Artemidorus, however, and accepted the note his former secretary was pushing into his hands and said he would read it. It is believed that Artemidorus had discovered the details of the murder plot and that his note was warning Caesar of the plan. It is said that Caesar still had the note with him when he died.

Spurinna, the fortune-teller who had warned him earlier about the Ides of March, was waiting for him at the entrance. Passing her, Caesar commented that the Ides of March had come and here he was. Spurinna replied, "They have come but they are not gone." Also at the entrance was a priest who had just killed an animal. The man reported that the guts of the animal did not predict good things. He then sacrificed another victim and found the same result. Impatient with this ancient custom, Caesar crossed the porch outside the Senate and entered. Did he notice that Trebonius, another traitor, was deep in conversation with Mark Antony in a senate waiting room? Trebonius delayed Antony, Caesar's trusted friend, so that Antony would not be waiting with all the other senators for Caesar's entrance into the Senate.

As Caesar sat down on his throne, all of the senators stood up. This was their usual way of respectfully greeting him. The plotters gathered in a half circle around him, hiding him from the other senators. One of the **assassins**, Tillius Cimber, asked Caesar to bring his brother back from **exile**. When Caesar refused to do this, Cimber stretched out his hand toward Caesar's toga as though he were begging him. When Caesar drew back, Cimber, as if turning from begging to anger, laid his hand on Caesar's purple toga and pulled it down from his shoulder. This was the signal to attack. However, it also had another meaning. By pulling down his purple robe, the assassins showed that Caesar was no longer the appointed dictator, but a senator like everyone else in the room. Caesar cried out, "But this is violence!" Casca, who was standing behind Caesar, quickly plunged his knife toward the dictator's neck but missed and cut through his shoulder. Caesar turned around, caught Casca's arm and stabbed it with his stylus, a tool that he carried for writing, crying out, "You villain, Casca! What are you about?"

Caesar was moving away when another assassin pierced him in the side and another cut his face. Then the assassins attacked him like a pack of wolves, one striking him in the thigh, another in the back. Caesar defended himself, lunging left and right with his stylus. He fought for his life, but the assassins, acting like maniacs, stabbed so wildly that they cut several of their own men. Finally, Caesar sank to the ground. It is said that at this moment Caesar saw Marcus Brutus coming toward him with a dagger in his hand. "And you too, my child!" were his last words. Covering his head with his toga, Caesar slowly died.

What happened after this dreadful act? Romans were in shock; the city seemed paralyzed. A day or two after Caesar's death, one of his cousins built an altar in the place where Caesar's body had lain. For six nights after the murder, a **comet** traced itself across the sky. People believed it was Caesar's spirit being taken to the heavens. Then a terrible war began, with Romans attacking other Romans. The fighting lasted for seventeen years until Octavius, Julius Caesar's grandnephew and adopted son, became emperor of Rome.

dictator *n.* a person who rules a country and its people without sharing power; in ancient Rome, a top public official who was usually appointed in cases of emergency and who had complete control of the government

Ides *n.* in the ancient Roman calendar, the fifteenth of March, May, July, and October, and the thirteenth of the other months

omen *n.* an event that is believed to be a sign of good or bad luck

tyrant *n.* someone who exercises power over others in a cruel and unjust manner

traitor *n.* a person who does something to harm his or her own country or friends

assassin *n.* a person who murders another, usually an important or famous person

exile *n.* the condition of being forced to leave one's native country

comet *n.* a bright object in space that is made up of ice, frozen gases, and dust particles; looks like a star with a long tail of light

LOOKING BACK AT WHAT YOU HAVE READ

1. Who was Julius Caesar?

____

____

2. Was Caesar a superstitious man? How do we know?

____

____

3. Why did Caesar's enemies want him dead?

____

____

4. Who were the Optimates?

____

____

5. Did Romans like the idea of having a king? Explain your answer.

____

____

6. Who was Marcus Brutus, and what role did he play in Caesar's murder?

7. Why was Mark Antony unable to help Caesar?

8. Why did the assassins want Caesar's murder to take place during the senate meeting on March 15?

WORKING WITH WORDS

Write a paragraph using four of the following vocabulary words.

dictator omen tyrant traitor exile assassin comet

In an **analogy**, you are trying to figure out the connection between two pairs of words.

Example: Rumor is to fact as friend is to ______________________.

First, you must understand the connection between the words in the first pair, rumor/fact. Make a picture in your mind of these words. Think how they are related. Then make a sentence describing what you see.

A rumor is *the opposite of* a fact.

Now use the word or words you have pictured to make the same connection between the second pair of words.

A friend is *the opposite of* an enemy.

The analogy, then, is rumor is to fact as friend is to enemy.

In the following analogies, decide what the connection is between the first pair of words. Make a picture of these words in your mind. Think how they are related. Next, write a word in the blank that will show the same connection between the second pair of words.

Armor is to metal as toga is to ______________________.

Ancient is to new as talkative is to ______________________.

Soldier is to fighting as author is to ______________________.

Fall is to bruise as cut is to ______________________.

Caesar is to Calpurina as husband is to ______________________.

Some words are spelled alike but have different meanings. These words are called **homographs.**

Example: A *pitcher* means the baseball player who throws the ball to the batter. It can also mean a container with a handle and a spout.

In the following sentences, the word in bold print has one meaning. Write what it is. Then write another meaning the word may have.

Julius Caesar's death would **change** the ancient world.

____

____

The talk **turned** to how they would like to die.

____

____

Caesar was so busy that he had no time to **rest**.

____

____

Before Caesar entered the Senate, he **spoke** to a fortune-teller.

____

____

Did the senators give Caesar a **hand** when he entered the Senate?

____

____

The assassins made sure that the knives were not **dull**.

____

____

For many Romans, the news of Caesar's death was hard to **swallow**.

____

____

WRITING SKILLS

Julius Caesar did not believe in fortune-tellers or omens. Do you believe in omens? Do you think that some people can predict the future? Write a paragraph giving your answer. Explain why you think what you do. Give examples, if possible. Be sure that your paragraph has a topic sentence, which gives the main idea of the paragraph, and a concluding sentence, which lets the reader know that you have finished your discussion.

First, write down some key ideas. When you have finished the paragraph, proofread your writing. Does it make sense? Have you included everything you wanted to say? Check it for correct spelling, grammar, capitalization, and punctuation.

Key ideas

Paragraph

Pretend you are Mark Antony, Caesar's trusted friend. Shortly after Caesar's death, you make a speech to the Senate about Caesar. What would you say? Write a speech about Caesar. Be sure that your speech has a topic sentence, which gives the main idea of the paragraph, and a concluding sentence, which lets the reader know that you have finished your discussion.

First, write down some key ideas. When you have finished the speech, proofread your writing. Does it make sense? Have you included everything you wanted to say? Check it for correct spelling, grammar, capitalization, and punctuation.

Key ideas

Speech:

AS YOU READ Put a ★ beside each important idea in the story. Then write in the margin why each is important. Put a ✓ next to parts of the story that you find interesting. Put a ? next to parts of the story you do not understand.

OTES

Maria Sibylla Merian was a remarkable person. She lived at a time when few women traveled on their own or worked as artists. Women were expected to stay at home, caring for their family. However, Merian was a gifted artist and **naturalist** whose work would completely change how scientists studied nature. Because of her excellent business ability, she was able to support herself and her family after her divorce. Even though women rarely made long trips by themselves for their work, Merian journeyed to a distant land to gather information and to record it through her drawings.

Merian was born in 1647 in Frankfurt am Main, which is now part of Germany. Her father, Mathias Merian, was an **engraver**, known throughout Europe. When she was three years old, he died and her mother married Jacob Marrel, a still-life painter, engraver, art teacher, and art dealer. Like all daughters, Merian was expected to stay at home until she married. Her mother taught her how to embroider and run a household. But at the same time, her stepfather taught her along with his male students how to draw, to make watercolors and still-life paintings, and to complete copper-plate engravings. Male artists at that time traveled to different workshops to get their training, but for a female to do this would not have been **proper**. Merian was fortunate that she could continue her education by studying the large collections of prints, books, and paintings that belonged to her family.

We do not know why, but Merian was also very interested in caterpillars. Perhaps she first noticed them in her stepfather's workshop. As a painter of still lifes, he probably often included them and other insects in his pictures of flowers. Merian said that she started observing insects when she was thirteen. She wrote, "From my youth onward I have been concerned with the study of insects. I began with silk-worms in my native city, Frankfurt am Main; then I observed the far more beautiful butterflies and moths that developed from other kinds of caterpillars. This led me to collect all the caterpillars I could find in order to study their **metamorphoses** . . . and to work at my painter's art so that I could sketch them from life and represent them in lifelike colors."

In 1665, she married Johann Andreas Graff, a favorite pupil of her stepfather. After their daughter Johanna Helena was born, the couple moved to Nuremberg, Graff's hometown. Then another daughter, Dorothea Maria, was born. Besides taking care of her children and embroidering, Merian painted on **parchment** and linen cloth, made engravings, and started teaching art to female students. She also continued observing insects, finding and sketching caterpillars in her garden as well as in different places in Nuremberg. Often, Merian brought insects to her workshop where she fed them plant leaves and recorded their behavior. Then she drew and painted them as they changed.

Merian's first book, *The New Flower Book,* was a catalog of flower engravings in three volumes. It came out between 1675 and 1680. People noticed that these drawings of flowers, with an insect included from time to time, were beautifully and accurately presented. Artists and embroiderers used them as a source for patterns and as models of flowers.

Her second book, *Wonderful* ***Transformation*** *and Singular Flower-Food of Caterpillars,* was published in 1679. Using only a magnifying glass as a tool, she drew 186 European moths, butterflies, and other insects, showing on a single page each insect in all stages of development. The insect was placed on or near the single plant upon which it fed and laid its eggs. Merian identified each plant with its German and Latin names; she wrote a page or two facing the picture explaining how her insect sample had looked and behaved at each stage. Often, she gave her reactions to its appearance, with exact dates for her comments. The book was amazing for the skill of its drawings and the nature of its content. It changed how naturalists and artists studied and recorded animal and plant life. This was because Merian drew and painted insects from life rather than from dead samples and because she showed the insects with the plants they ate changing over time.

In 1685, Merian joined the Labadists, a religious group that believed people should not own anything. Leaving her husband, but taking her mother and two daughters with her, she moved to a Labadist community in Friesland, near the North

Sea. There she worked on whatever jobs the community assigned her, but she also continued searching for caterpillars and moths and began studying frogs.

By 1690, Merian no longer practiced Labadism. After gaining a divorce from her husband, which was at that time a very unusual step for a woman, she moved with her daughters to Amsterdam. She began teaching and painting again in this large thriving city. Soon people were buying her watercolors of flowers, birds, and insects. Merian continued working with caterpillars and started observing other insects. She became acquainted with naturalists and collectors in the city, who welcomed her into their group.

Seeing collections of foreign insects in museums and in private collections, she noticed that none of them, including her own, showed the origins and later transformations of foreign insects. So as Merian wrote, "I was moved to take a long and costly journey to Suriname."

Merian's trip to this Dutch colony in South America was very unusual: first, because she was a woman and, in addition, because she was going for her work. Some naturalists had jobs in the colonies, and a few traveled to South America with wealthy people who paid them. Merian, however, was organizing and paying for her own trip. To raise money, she sold a large collection of her paintings as well as many of her insect **specimens**. She hoped that when she returned to Amsterdam she would be able to sell rare examples of insects that she found in Suriname.

Merian and her daughter Dorothea arrived in Suriname in 1699 and settled into a house in Paramaribo, the major town. She began work immediately to find and record new insect life in her own garden and in the forest right outside Paramaribo. When she wanted to explore areas farther away, she found the African slaves and the native people, or Amerindians, very helpful. In 1700, she took her first trip inland, which began with a forty-mile paddle upstream to a plantation during the rainy season.

Merian discussed insects and plant use with the Amerindians and Africans. They brought her many specimens that they thought she might be interested in seeing. One amazing example was a large group of lantern flies, with their glowing light and unusual music. Merian also studied spiders, birds, lizards, snakes, and toads.

Her methods were similar to those she had used in Europe. First, she sketched everything from life, and then she and Dorothea made paintings on parchment of the caterpillars, the cocoons, and their food. Next, she preserved the butterflies, moths, and beetles in brandy or pressed them so that they could be grouped with their larvae. She planned to paint them later. Merian never got used to the heat in Suriname, and after almost two years she and Dorothea returned to Amsterdam. Before she left, she arranged with someone she knew to send her specimens so that she could sell them.

Once she returned, Merian supported herself by selling some of the insects she had collected. In 1705, her book *Metamorphosis of the Insects of Suriname* appeared in Amsterdam. It showed beautiful illustrations of plants and insects that were completely unknown to most people in Europe. Unlike other naturalists of her time, Merian gave credit to the Africans and Amerindians who had helped her find plants and insects and who gave her important information about them. The book was so popular that another edition came out in 1719, two years after her death.

Merian's scientific and artistic work became well known in several countries. People came to Amsterdam to visit her and to buy her drawings and engravings. In 1711 one visitor, a scholar from Frankfurt, wrote, "She is sixty-two years old, but still very lively . . . and hard-working, a very courteous woman." When Czar Peter the Great from Russia arrived in Amsterdam, he had his doctor call on her and buy some of her paintings. In the last years of her life, Merian worked on preparing a Dutch-language version of her European *Caterpillars*. When Merian died in 1717, Dorothea sold all of her mother's pictures, engravings, plates, and texts to a publisher in Amsterdam, who translated her work into other languages. Long after she died, Maria Sibylla Merian's careful notes and drawings continued to contribute to art and to science. Her paintings and prints of flowers, fruit, and insects were not forgotten.

naturalist *n.* a person who studies plants and animals, especially those that are living

engraver *n.* a person who cuts or etches letters or designs on a hard surface such as a metal plate or a wooden block

proper *adj.* suitable; appropriate

metamorphosis *n., pl.* **metamorphoses** a complete change in appearance or form, as the one that occurs when a caterpillar becomes a butterfly

parchment *n.* the skin of a sheep or goat, prepared as a material to write on

transformation *n.* the act of being greatly changed in shape, form, or appearance

specimen *n.* one of a group of things that can be taken to represent the group

LOOKING BACK AT WHAT YOU HAVE READ

1. Why was Merian able to support herself and her family?

2. What do you think it might have been like to be one of Merian's daughters?

3. Why do you think Merian decided to become an artist?

4. For her times, Merian was an unusual person. What was it in Merian's background and upbringing that allowed her to become such a person?

5. How old was Merian when she went to Suriname?

6. In Merian's time many people liked her paintings and drawings because of their exact scientific details. Today, her works about insects are admired for their beauty. Why do you think we look at her work differently now?

___

___

___

7. Why was Merian's book *Wonderful Transformation and Singular Flower-Food of Caterpillars* so important?

___

___

8. What part of Merian's life was most interesting to you? Explain your answer.

___

___

___

WORKING WITH WORDS

Write down four words from the story whose meaning you do not know. If a word is not a vocabulary word, look up the definition and write it down. Use each of the words in a sentence.

Do you remember that a **metaphor** is a phrase that compares two things that are not alike but does not use the words *like* or *as*? Here are two examples.

My dad says that I am *a late bloomer*.

The fog was *a blanket* covering the coast.

Below are some metaphors describing events in Merian's life. Rewrite the sentences, using your own metaphors.

During the forty-mile paddle upstream, a half-hour rest was *a cool drink*.

The trees in the jungle were *a green tent*, under which Merian and her helpers searched for insects.

When faced with a problem, Merian was *a lion in battle*.

____

____

For many women, Merian's life was *a cool wind of change.*

____

____

In an **analogy**, you are trying to figure out the connection between two pairs of words.

Example: Painter is to brush as photographer is to ______________ .

First, you must understand the connection between the words in the first pair, painter/brush. Make a picture in your mind of these words. Think how they are related. Then make a sentence describing what you see.

A painter *uses* a brush for work.

Now use the word you have pictured to make the same connection between the second pair of words.

A photographer *uses* a camera for work.

The analogy, then, is painter is to brush as photographer is to camera.

In the following analogies, decide what the connection is between the first pair of words. Make a picture of these words in your mind. Think how they are related. Next, write a word in the blank that will show the same connection between the second pair of words.

Energetic is to lively as courteous is to ______________.

Suriname is to South America as Germany is to ______________.

Marry is to divorce as distant is to ______________.

Seed is to plant as caterpillar is to ______________.

Moth is to bee as collie is to ______________.

Ship is to captain as city is to ______________.

Write a paragraph summarizing the important events of Maria Sibylla Merian's life. Put the events in chronological order. Be sure that your paragraph has a topic sentence, which gives the main idea of the paragraph, and a concluding sentence, which lets the reader know that you have finished your discussion.

First, write down some key ideas. When you have finished the paragraph, proofread your writing. Does it make sense? Have you included everything you wanted to say? Check it for correct spelling, grammar, capitalization, and punctuation.

Key ideas

Maria Sibylla Merian's Life

An **expanded paragraph** is one in which you use several supporting ideas to develop your main idea. To make your meaning clear, you should use **transition words**. These words give the signal that you have finished discussing one supporting idea and are ready to move to the next. Remember that these words are always followed by a comma. Here are some common transition words.

first second next last finally

Merian had a productive, interesting life. Write an expanded paragraph about what you would like your life to be like when you become an adult. How would you like to live? What would you like to do? What would you like to achieve? Try to use at least three of the transition words above. Be sure that your paragraph has a topic sentence, which gives the main idea of the paragraph, and a concluding sentence, which lets the reader know that you have finished your discussion.

First, write down some key ideas. When you have finished the paragraph, proofread your writing. Does it make sense? Have you included everything you wanted to say? Check it for correct spelling, grammar, capitalization, and punctuation.

Key ideas

Title:

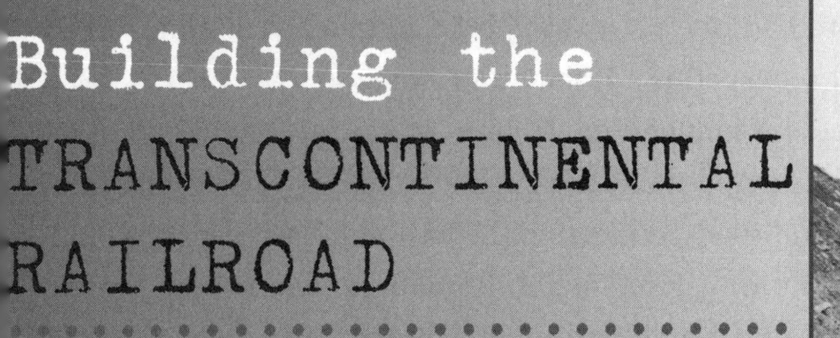

Building the TRANSCONTINENTAL RAILROAD

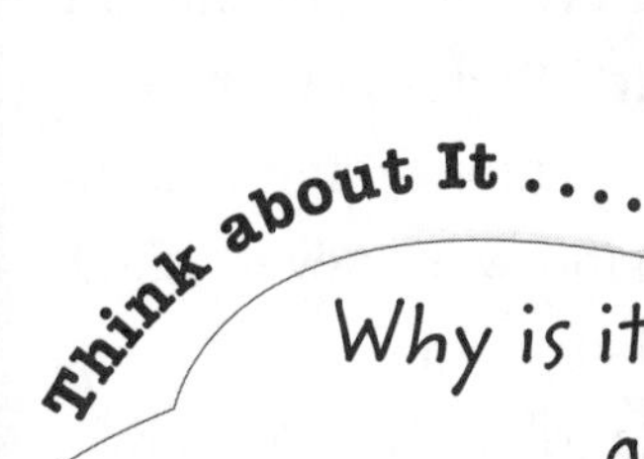

Why is it important for a country to have a good transportation system?

____

____

AS YOU READ Put a ★ beside each important idea in the story. Then write in the margin why each is important. Put a ✓ next to parts of the story that you find interesting. Put a **?** next to parts of the story you do not understand.

OTES

In 1869, the United States, then a very young nation, became the first country to build a **transcontinental** railroad to link the country's east and west coasts. Until that time, people used carriages and stagecoaches to travel across the continent. Businesses badly needed railroads so that products from the West could be sent to markets on the East Coast or in Europe and so that people living in the West could also receive goods from the eastern states. California had become a state in 1850, but it did not feel part of the country because it was far from the other states. People living in California imported everything by ship, an expensive and very lengthy process. There were some trains, but they ran from the East Coast only as far as Chicago, Illinois.

The transcontinental railroad, which was to run from Omaha, Nebraska, to Sacramento, California, would not only allow products to be shipped by train but also enable people to travel across the country. Without a railroad, the trip across the continent was dangerous and very long. Railroads would allow army troops, supplies, and mail to move faster and more cheaply. In addition, they would lessen the need to maintain the many forts across the country, which protected the increasing number of settlers from attacks by the Native Americans who lived on that land.

Worldwide, the transcontinental railroad was the biggest engineering **feat** of the nineteenth century. Never before had one project required so much planning and so many workers. How it was accomplished is a fascinating story.

Thousands of people completed a tremendous amount of work to build this railroad. The man who could be considered the driving force behind it was Abraham Lincoln. Lincoln believed that a railroad connecting the east and west coasts would unite the country in more than one way. He thought the railroad would be a "never failing source of communication" that would not be interrupted by freezing weather or high or low water. He realized that the railroad would be a means of holding the Pacific Coast to the Union. Once he became president, he did everything he could to make sure that the railroad was built. The support of the United States government was essential for this project, since only the government had the money and land to pay for it. However, the Native Americans who lived on this land were never asked for or paid for the use of the land, which they thought of as their own.

In 1862, Congress passed and Lincoln signed the Pacific Railroad Act. This law gave the job of building the railroad to two companies. The Central Pacific Railroad, in the West, was to lay track eastward from Sacramento, California. It had already found a pass through the Sierra Nevada and had mapped the proposed route. The Union Pacific Railroad would start laying track westward from a point near Omaha. Rail lines already existed that ran from the East Coast to Chicago. These would be extended to meet the new railroad at Omaha. The railroads would receive fixed amounts from the government for laying the tracks on the land that it made available. The companies would be paid $16,000 per mile for laying tracks on flat land, $32,000 per mile for tracks in the foothills of the mountains, and $48,000 per mile for those across mountains. The government also gave them wood, stones, and earth to construct stations and other buildings near the tracks.

The two companies had to hire the people who would do the actual building. The Central Pacific hired thousands of workers, many of them Chinese immigrants who had been living in California; the Union Pacific hired European **immigrants** who lived in the cities of the East Coast and, once the war was over, Civil War **veterans**.

The workers of the Central Pacific had to dig tunnels through miles of granite, an extremely hard rock, and build bridges over deep valleys, which became raging torrents after each rainstorm and in the spring when the snow in the mountains melted. The Central Pacific workers had to cross the Sierra Nevada. Blasting miles of tunnels through such wide, solid granite mountains had never been done before.

The Union Pacific workers, laying rails from the east, would have to cross the Rocky Mountains and the Wasatch Range. Along the way, they would cross great stretches of desert where there was neither water nor wild animals that they could hunt for food. They worked on land that had no trees, which they needed for making rail **ties** and for building bridges. All their supplies were brought up the Missouri River and then sent on rail to wherever the men were working. In 1866, forty

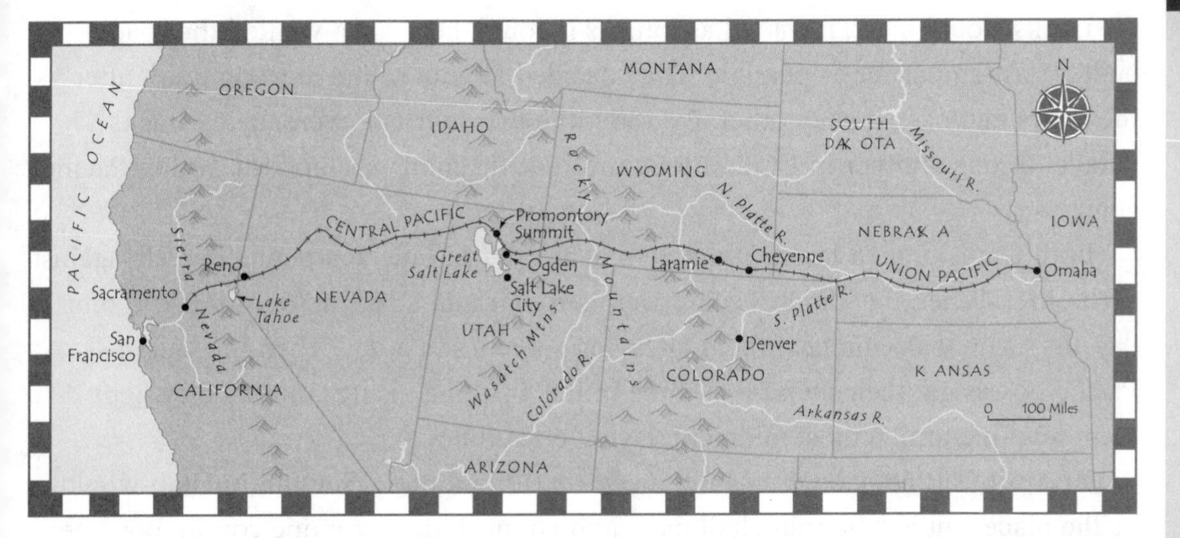

railroad cars brought in the rails, ties, bridging, fastenings, fuel, and other supplies for the Union Pacific men and their animals. About five hundred cows owned by the company grazed along the tracks. They were used to feed the workers. A meal usually consisted of pans of soup, platters of potatoes, fried, roasted, or boiled meat, pitchers of steaming coffee, and sometimes canned fruit and pies or cakes.

In some areas, Native Americans, who saw their land taken over, attacked the workers. The aim of the native people was to stop them and to take their supplies–livestock, rifles, ammunition, hats, jackets, and food. Since the army did not have enough soldiers to defend the workers, the men often had to protect themselves. All were armed with guns. Nevertheless, Native American raiding parties were difficult to avoid.

Both railroads worked through all sorts of weather, including some of the worst snowstorms of the nineteenth century. The men built sheds to cover the tracks, but sometimes there was so much snow that they had to sit and wait out the storm. In the desert, the temperatures could rise above one hundred degrees.

The transcontinental railroad could not have been done without the wonderful spirit of the workers. One **surveyor** wrote in his diary, "What unites them all is a fierce determination not to let down those coming on behind. . . . They all knew and accepted that every man was dependent on every other man." Whether they were Central Pacific or Union Pacific workers, their major characteristic was how hard they worked. Unlike today, almost everything was done by muscle power because there was no electricity or even steam power to help them. It was the last great building project done mostly by hand. The dirt excavated for cuts through ridges was removed one handcart at a time. The dirt for filling a gorge was brought in by handcart. Some of the areas to fill were hundreds of feet high and a quarter mile or more in length. In addition, they had to keep the **grade** as even as possible at all times.

As the Union Pacific came out of Nebraska to begin its attack on Wyoming and the Central Pacific worked the Sierra Nevada, the railroads' race toward each other became headline news. Even though Congress had the right to pick the place where the tracks would meet, it waited as long as it could, because it wanted the roads built as fast and as far as possible. They decided to choose the meeting point after the crews had passed each other. By 1869, the two railroads were laying tracks parallel to one another in Utah, the Central Pacific going east and the Union Pacific going west.

Both teams of men laid track at an amazingly fast rate, competing fiercely against each other. When the Union Pacific men laid four and a half miles of track in one day, the Central Pacific beat them by laying six miles in a day. Then the Union Pacific bosses got their men up at three in the morning; using lanterns they kept them working until almost midnight, laying eight miles.

On April 9, 1869, Congress announced that Promontory Summit in Utah would be the place where "the rails shall meet and connect and form one continuous line." The Central Pacific rested until April 27, when they had only fourteen miles to go and the Union Pacific had nine. By seven o'clock that evening, the Central Pacific workers had laid ten miles of track. An army officer who witnessed it said, "I never saw such an organization as this; it is just like an army marching across over the ground and leaving a track built behind them." Never before or since has railroad track been laid so quickly. On April 30, 1869, the Central Pacific Railroad was the first to arrive at the meeting point in Utah.

On May 10, 1869, a crowd of people gathered at Promontory Summit, Utah, where the tracks of the two railroads met. To connect the last rail, a golden spike, six inches long, was driven into the final rail tie. One telegraph wire was attached to the golden **spike** and another to a sledgehammer. As the hammer tapped in the golden spike, the telegraph lines sent the news nationwide, "DONE!" People celebrated across the nation. Chicago had the biggest parade of the century, seven miles long; Philadelphia rang the Liberty Bell.

Less than a week after the event, people were riding the train from New York to San Francisco in seven days. Mail that once had cost dollars per ounce and took forever now cost only pennies and traveled cross-country in a few days. Lincoln's dream of a country united from coast to coast was now a reality.

transcontinental *adj.* crossing a continent

feat *n.* an act or deed that shows great courage, strength, or skill

immigrant *n.* a person who leaves one country and settles in another

veteran *n.* a person who has served in the armed forces

tie *n.* one of the pieces of wood that are laid across and underneath railroad tracks

surveyor *n.* a person whose work is measuring land to fix or find out its boundaries

grade *n.* the amount of slope or angle on a hill, road, or railroad track

spike *n.* a large, heavy nail

LOOKING BACK AT WHAT YOU HAVE READ

1. What was the Pacific Railroad Act and why was it important?

___

___

2. Why were President Lincoln and other people in the government interested in building a transcontinental railroad?

___

___

3. What did the government do to help the two railroad companies that were attempting to build a railroad across the continent?

___

___

4. Who were the workers for the Central Pacific and the Union Pacific railroads?

___

___

5. In which states did the Central Pacific and the Union Pacific lay their tracks?

___

___

6. What was so amazing about how the tracks were laid?

7. Why was the Missouri River important in the building of the transcontinental railroad?

8. How did the transcontinental railroad affect people in the West?

WORKING WITH WORDS

You remember that **homophones** are words that sound alike but are spelled differently and have different meanings.

Example: *pedal* and *peddle*

The bicycle rider found it very difficult to *pedal* against the wind.

During every baseball game, people *peddle* drinks and food.

The words in the box are homophones. Use them to fill in the blanks. Each sentence contains a homophone pair.

soar	**heel**	**sum**	**days**	**steak**
they're	**daze**	**tents**	**their**	**sore**
some	**stake**	**heal**	**tense**	**there**

What was the price for building the transcontinental railroad? It was ______________________

______________________!

What did a foot doctor do for a man working on the railroad? He would ______________

his ______________________.

When the two railroads were working side by side, newspapers reported,

"______________________ both ______________________!"

As the end of the race neared, the workers in the ______________________ became more and

more ______________________.

After a worker drove in a ______________________, he felt like eating a

______________________.

Even though the bodies of the Central Pacific workers were very ______________________,

their spirits started to ______________________ when they realized they had reached the

meeting point first.

The building of the transcontinental railroad was such an amazing accomplishment that

some people were in a ______________________ for several ______________________ after

hearing the news.

You remember that a **proverb** is a short saying that expresses something that many people believe to be true. "Look before you leap" is a proverb. It means that you have to consider every angle of a situation carefully before you act.

Explain how the building of the transcontinental railroad is an example of the proverb "Fact is stranger than fiction."

____

____

____

Explain why officials of the Union Pacific Railroad would agree with the proverb "There's many a slip between cup and lip."

Explain how the building of the transcontinental railroad is an example of the proverb "Time is money."

CROSSWORD PUZZLE

Use the clues to fill in the puzzle. Then check your answers with each clue. Do they make sense?

Down

1. Another word for *join*

3. Crossing a continent

5. The opposite of *difficult*

6. The last one was tapped in place on May 10, 1869.

7. An extremely hard rock

9. The Native Americans made ____ on the workers.

12. They worked for the Central Pacific.

13. He strongly supported building the railroad.

15. The workers experienced some of the ____ snowstorms of the century.

17. The Union Pacific began to build west from this city.

Across

1. The rail lines met in this state.

2. One mountain range the railroad had to cross

4. They were Union Pacific workers after the Civil War ended.

8. A word that means "a great achievement"

10. The rails a train runs on

11. The railroad was the last great project built almost completely by ____.

14. People who moved to the United States

16. This describes the last spike.

18. The Central Pacific built in this direction.

19. The Central Pacific workers had to dig these through the mountains.

20. This was what was built to connect the east and west coasts.

WRITING SKILLS

Write a paragraph summarizing the important steps in the building of the transcontinental railroad. Remember to put the events in chronological order. Be sure that your paragraph has a topic sentence, which gives the main idea of the paragraph, and a concluding sentence, which lets the reader know that you have finished your discussion.

First, write down some key ideas. When you have finished the paragraph, proofread your writing. Does it make sense? Have you included everything you wanted to say? Check it for correct spelling, grammar, capitalization, and punctuation.

Key ideas

____

____

____

____

Building the Transcontinental Railroad

Pretend you are living in 1870, soon after the first transcontinental railroad was completed. Write a four-paragraph story telling how this affected your daily life. Put your supporting ideas into separate paragraphs. Make certain that each supporting paragraph has its own topic sentence. You need one paragraph each for your introduction and conclusion. Be sure to include a title.

First, write an outline for your composition. When you have finished your composition, proofread your writing. Does it make sense? Have you included everything you wanted to say? Check it for correct spelling, grammar, capitalization, and punctuation.

Outline

Introduction

Paragraph 1

Paragraph 2

Conclusion

Title: